A DYNAMIC ESTUARY
MAN, NATURE AND THE HUMBER

Hull University Press

LAMPADA FERENS

A DYNAMIC ESTUARY
MAN, NATURE AND THE HUMBER

Edited by

N.V. JONES

Director
Institute of Estuarine and
Coastal Studies
University of Hull

HULL UNIVERSITY PRESS
1988

© Hull University Press

British Library Cataloguing in Publication Data

A dynamic estuary: man, nature and the Humber
  1. Humber, River (England)
  I. Jones, N.V.
  551.46'1336   GC601

ISBN 0-85958-469-0

Phototypeset in 11 on 12pt Times and printed by the Central Print Unit, the University of Hull and bound by Khromatec Ltd.

Contents

Preface

The Humber is the heart of Humberside in more than just name. It is the most obvious geographical feature of the region and has been, and continues to be, an important resource. Man has settled its banks and navigated its waters since he was capable of doing either in this part of the world and he has exploited its other attractions up to the present day. He will, no doubt, continue to do so as the waterway is still a most valuable resource at both local and national level.

The estuary is surrounded by a large area of flat land and offers access to the inland waterways and is strategically placed with respect to trade with the European Community and other northern European countries as well as the North Sea gas and oil fields. The area is now well served with motorway links to the rest of Britain and, of course, the two banks of the river are joined by the magnificent Humber Bridge. The estuary is also an important habitat for wildlife which has resulted in most of its banks being designated Sites of Special Scientific Interest, nature reserves, country parks or wildfowl refuge.

It would be reasonable to expect that such an important feature is well studied and that much information about its various aspects is readily available. In fact, this is not the case. There exist a few summary documents dealing with particular aspects of the estuary but little of broader interest has been published. This book brings together a range of topics in an attempt to increase interest in the estuary by making the material easily available to the residents of its banks as well as to visitors to the area.

The publication arises out of a series of lectures given by members of the Institute of Estuarine and Coastal Studies at the University of Hull. The series was part of the programme offered by the Department (now School) of Adult and Continuing Education of the University, first given in Hull and later repeated in Grimsby. The course was well received by the students but it exposed the lack of readily available information on the river and its features. It was decided, therefore, to try to remedy this situation by publishing a series of papers based on the lectures.

An approach was made to Humberside County Council to solicit support for the venture which resulted in the Leisure

Services Department accepting it as one of its projects. This was a great encouragement and the book is now produced by the Hull University Press with the support of the County Council, a joint venture which seems particularly appropriate for this subject.

The theme of the book is the changing estuary and man. The first four chapters deal with the natural features of the estuary although man has influenced the present coastline. The remaining chapters deal with some aspects of man's activities on and around the river. As a biologist I have found the Humber to be a most fascinating river with plenty of life and interest as well as an atmosphere of its own. The mixture of water and vast skies of the outer estuary is awe-inspiring and the more constrained scenery of the upper estuary, including the bridge, is impressive for quite different reasons. I have also found the material provided by my colleagues to be most interesting and this has added an extra dimension to my fascination with the river. I hope that you also find the whole, or even a part, of the volume of interest and that we can share the fascination of this unique waterway.

Publications such as this one which is based on the work of several authors are often criticised for their discontinuity of style. This is even more likely than usual in this case as it includes the writings of authors from diverse disciplines. Although an attempt has been made to standardise presentation each author has followed the conventions normal for the discipline. I apologise to you at this stage if this affects your reading of the volume! It is, however, meant to be a multi-disciplinary work reflecting the activities of the Institute of Estuarine and Coastal Studies as well as the many facets of the Humber.

N.V. Jones
Institute of Estuarine and Coastal Studies
University of Hull

February 1988

List of Figures

List of Plates

(centre fold)

Plate 1   Aerial view of Welwick salt-marsh showing the distinctively-zoned vegetation.

Plate 2   Salt-marsh development at the base of the Spurn peninsula.
(a)   1962 — scattered islands of *Spartina*.
(b)   1985 — same location — well-established *Puccinellia* community in the foreground fringed by *Spartina* in the background, still extending into Spurn Bight.

Plate 3   Salt-marsh plants.
(a)   *Salicornia* and *Suaeda* dominate the foreground; *Spartina*, the background.
(b)   *Spartina anglica* in flower.
(c)   Sea-lavender (*Limonium vulgare*) in full-bloom.
(d)   Foreground — Sea purslane (*Halimione portulacoides*)
Background — Sea lavender.

Plate 4   Estuarine invertebrates.
(a)   *Macoma balthica* (Baltic tellin)
(b)   *Cerastoderma edule* (The cockle)
(c)   *Nereis diversicolor* (The ragworm)
(d)   *Hydrobia ulvae* (Mud snail) on mud

Plate 5   Estuarine fish and birds.
(a)   *Liparis montagui* (Sea Snail)
(b)   *Syngnathus acus* (Greater Pipefish)
(c)   *Pomatoschistus microps* (Goby)
(d)   A flock of waders.

Plate 6   Part of the Burleigh chart of the Humber, showing sandbanks and the position and depth in fathoms of the navigation channel (*c.* 1560).

List of Tables

List of Contributors
with their affiliation to the University of Hull

W. Armstrong   Reader in the Department of Plant Biology and Genetics.

Joyce Bellamy   Honorary Fellow in the Department of Economic and Social History.

G. de Boer   Reader Emeritus in the Department of Geography.

A.M. Ferrar   Fellow of the University and former Map Curator in the Department of Geography.

Anne Goodall   Research Student in the Department of Zoology.

N.V. Jones   Senior Lecturer and Head of the Department of Zoology. Director of the Institute of Estuarine and Coastal Studies.

P.N. Jones   Senior Lecturer in the Department of Geography.

D.B. Lewis   Lecturer in the School of Adult and Continuing Education.

J.W. Neale   Professor of Micropalaeontology in the Department of Geology.

J. North   Lecturer in the Department of Geography.

J.S. Pethick   Senior Lecturer in the Department of Geography.

Acknowledgements

It is a pleasure to express my thanks to all the authors who have so readily contributed to this volume. It is one thing to deliver a lecture but it is another to produce a paper!

My thanks also go to the School of Adult and Continuing Education for encouraging the venture and organising the course of lectures in the first place.

Particular thanks are due to Humberside County Council Leisure Services Department for their support and especially Mr Peter Ainscough for his assistance and enthusiasm for the project.

I also express my sincere thanks to Hull University Press, particularly Jean Smith, Joyce Bellamy, Alan Best, Barbara Nield and Jackie Horton for their interest, encouragement, patience and constructive criticism.

I also acknowledge the following for giving permission to reproduce illustrations:

The Wardens and Bretheren of the Corporation of the Hull Trinity House for Figures 5.2 and 5.3.

The British Museum for Figure 5.1 and Plate 6.

The Humber Estuary Committee for Figures 4.3, 4.4, 4.5 and Table 4.1.

Humberside County Council Economic Development Unit for the cover.

Roland Wheeler-Osman, Roger Key and the authors for material for the coloured plates.

I

The geology of the Humber area

J.W. Neale

Introduction

The geology forms the backcloth on which the Humber is developed and which controls its course and content of particulate and dissolved material. Technically the Humber is that part of the Trent-Ouse drainage system below the confluence of those rivers

1

and as such has a course of some 62km (40 miles) or so from Alkborough to the sea at Spurn Point. In draining almost a fifth of England, the content of the Humber, however, is very much a reflection of the input from the diverse Trent and Ouse drainages and the deposits over which they run and, before turning to the Humber in its strict sense, a brief reference may be made to the geology of its two main tributaries.

The Trent is largely a lowland system draining large parts of the English Midlands although it does draw some of its water from tributaries rising on the Carboniferous rocks of the Derbyshire moors in the west and others draining the Jurassic scarp to the east (Fig.1.1). For much of its course it runs over the New Red Sandstone rocks of the Permian and Triassic Systems formed between 286 and 213 million years ago which, particularly in the Vale of Trent, are often overlain by glacial and superficial deposits. The New Red Sandstone, well seen around Nottingham and elsewhere, lives up to its name and consists largely of orange to brick-red sandstones, silts and mudstones which owe their colour to iron oxide (usually haematite) which coats the grains. These rocks were formed in an arid environment reminiscent of some of the North African upland areas at the present day. Besides the sandstones, the deposits are largely fluviatile or lacustrine, the result of flash floods sweeping debris down from the higher areas into the lowlands. Prolonged periods of rainfall produced lakes and the evaporation of these standing bodies of water gave rise to deposits of gypsum and salt. The 'alabaster' (gypsum) industry of places like Tutbury was well known in the past for its carvings and bas reliefs and the gypsum carried into the Trent gives it that hardness and other properties which determined the growth of Burton upon Trent as a major brewing centre. Besides this hardness carried in solution, the Trent system also carries a large load of sediment in suspension which is mainly derived from the New Red Rocks or the overlying superficial deposits which are themselves principally formed from the same source.

The Ouse system drains the more northerly area and in the Vale of York and Vale of Mowbray flows over similar rocks to those discussed above. The gypsum bands in the New Red Sandstones seen by the River Ure at Ripon and petrifying wells at Knaresborough are all reminiscent of the situation seen in the Trent system and Tadcaster, with its brewing industry and sited on

2

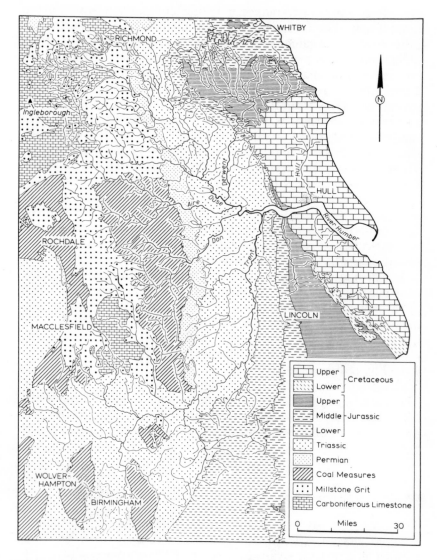

Figure 1.1   Map of the solid geology of the Humber drainage area.

New Red Sandstone, makes a fitting comparison with Burton upon Trent. The Ouse system has a much greater proportion of other rocks in its catchment area, however, and these include both older and younger rocks. In the Pennines, much of the early courses of the major rivers flowing to join the Ouse lies on Carboniferous rocks formed between 380 and 286 million years ago. These range from the large tracts of pale grey Carboniferous Limestone well seen at places like the Buttertubs, to the hard sandstone and softer shaly and coaly rocks of the Millstone Grit and Coal Measures making up great tracts of peaty moorland. These all make their distinctive contribution to the waters of the Ouse as it goes to join the Humber. To the east of the Vale of York and Vale of Mowbray the Derwent system drains an area of younger Jurassic rocks before joining the Ouse. The fact that the Derwent now joins a system which flows out through the Humber is a reflection of changes brought about by events of relatively recent date which will be dealt with later.

The geology of the Humber is most conveniently covered under four headings namely 1) the solid rocks of the Mesozoic Systems, 2) the Tertiary Interval, 3) the Pleistocene Ice Age and 4) Subsequent history.

1. The solid rocks

These are largely covered by superficial deposits and belong to the Mesozoic Era. The rocks consist of bedded sediments formed under varying conditions and with a general easterly dip at a gentle angle.

(i) The Triassic rocks

These form the higher part of the New Red Sandstone and formed between 248 and 213 million years ago. They consist of rocks formed under arid, oxidising conditions as outlined above and underlie much of the Vale of Trent and Vale of York. In the Humber area they consist mostly of fine-grained red mudstones (Mercian Mudstones = Keuper Marls) which erode easily and are covered by later superficial deposits.

4

The Rhaetic (formerly placed in the Jurassic System) is now considered to be the topmost Trias and is always thin, reaching a
maximum thickness of about 20m. The beds are fine-grained,
laminated, dark-grey or black shales and clays which show
reddish-brown horizons in some of the upper beds. Occasional
dark grey impure limestones are also developed. These beds yield
molluscs such as *Pteria contorta* and, although conditions were
not yet well enough established for the appearance of ammonites,
show the first entry of the sea into the area after the preceding
continental regime. The beds are poorly exposed and best seen at
Alkborough and elsewhere south of the river where they form a
narrow strip at the foot of the Jurassic escarpment.

(ii)   The Jurassic rocks

These were deposited between 213 and 144 million years ago and
show a threefold division into Lower, Middle and Upper.
   Like the rocks below they dip eastwards at a low angle but their
disposition is affected by the Market Weighton Structure. This
formed a positive area, variously known as an Upwarp, Block or
Axis, during Jurassic and early Cretaceous times.

(a)   The Lower Jurassic (The Lias)

These beds consist largely of marine clays and shales and
again show a threefold division into Lower, Middle and
Upper. Marine conditions are now very well established, the
fauna is abundant and diverse, and the ammonites first
appear a short distance above the base.

The Lower Lias
This contains some thin limestone bands which help to form
the scarp which stands out above the Trent to the south and
forms the westwards facing scarp through North Cave and
North Cliffe to the north. The most important bed, however,
is the Scunthorpe Ironstone which forms the marked feature
on which Scunthorpe stands. This is an oolitic ironstone with
a very considerable fossil content which provides enough lime
to make this virtually a self-fluxing ore. The ironstone

reaches a maximum thickness of 10m and is restricted to a distance of about 16km along the strike. Its oolitic nature and large fossil content suggest strong current activity, good oxygenation and a shallow sea floor at this time but the conditions of deposition of this type of sedimentary iron ore are not fully understood.

The Middle Lias
This consists of fine grained marine clays with overlying flaggy limestone and ferruginous sandstone which thin rapidly northwards through Lincolnshire. Only the upper part extends north of the river where about 3m of beds have been seen in the past near Everthorpe.

The Upper Lias
The blue-grey clays and shales of this division are poorly exposed, thin northwards and like the preceding Middle Lias disappear over the Market Weighton Structure. The beds themselves are fully marine and yield ammonites and other mollusca.

(b)   The Middle Jurassic

In Middle Jurassic times England as a whole showed evidence of uplift and general shallowing of the sea so that deposits in this area consist of a mixture of rocks deposited under deltaic conditions (at one time known as 'The Estuarine Series') and true marine, albeit shallow marine, deposits. Overall these rocks are relatively thin in this area and poorly exposed except for the best developed of the marine horizons. This is the shallow water, brashy and oolitic limestone which forms Lincoln Edge and its continuation northwards and is known as the Lincolnshire Limestone south of the river and the Cave Oolite north of the river. This forms a marked scarp feature and has been used locally as a building stone as seen in many of the houses and churches in villages along its outcrop and in extensive dry stone walling. It is also a considerable source of hard core so that it is well exposed in a number of quarries from Kirton in Lindsey to North Newbald and Sancton where it disappears under overlying rocks and only appears north of

6

the Market Weighton Structure where it is known as 'the Millepore Bed'.

South of the river the Middle Jurassic beds above the Cave Oolite show a varied succession which is brought to a close by the Cornbrash, a thin rubbly limestone no more than 2m thick whose upper part is referred to the Callovian Stage of the Upper Jurassic. North of the river the Cornbrash has not been found and a series of white sands lies above the Cave Oolite.

(c)   The Upper Jurassic

The Upper Cornbrash (in Lincolnshire), the White Sands and the overlying Kellaways Sandstone represent the start of the great Callovian transgression. The Kellaways Sandstone shows a remarkably rich and varied fauna consistent with a littoral shallow water area. This sequence of sands and sandstone forms a minor but useful source of water supply in the area. Following their deposition the sea deepened, sedimentation became more uniform and is represented by the thick sequence of Oxford, Ampthill and Kimmeridge Clays. These grey, blue-grey or black fine-grained rocks floor the Vale of Ancholme and like their predecessors thin northwards and are last seen immediately north of the village of North Newbald where they disappear beneath the chalk as they approach the Market Weighton Structure. The Ampthill Clay was formerly worked in the Welton Quarry in connection with the Cement Works at Melton where it was mixed with the chalk before calcining. The Kimmeridge Clay, while of no commercial significance in the area, provides the south pier of the Humber Bridge. It was the intrinsic properties of this rock which caused the problems which led to an eighteen month delay in the progress of construction. The best section in the area is to be seen in the quarry at South Ferriby.

(iii) The Cretaceous rocks

(a) The Lower Cretaceous

In south Lincolnshire this shows a varied sequence of marine sediments formed between 144 and 98 million years ago. The earliest Cretaceous, the Upper Spilsby Sandstone lying above the mid-Spilsby nodule bed, gives way to the oolitic Claxby Ironstone which in turn is overlain by the Tealby Clays and limestones. The succeeding fine-grained rocks, essentially clays with some iron ooliths in their lower part, give way in late Lower Cretaceous time to a coarse, orange, ferruginous sandstone known as the Carstone and the thin, overlying Red Chalk. These beds thin rapidly northwards and only the Carstone and Red Chalk are known north of the river. These are the first beds to get across the Market Weighton Structure and may be seen at Goodmanham where a few inches of Carstone overlain by three feet of Red Chalk rest on a horizon low down in the Lower Lias.

(b) The Upper Cretaceous

In England the previous 100 million years was a consistent story of relatively shallow seas, which at times became shallow enough to allow the development of deltas and even swamp areas with plants which were sometimes abundant enough to give rise to thin coaly layers. The Red Chalk at the top of the Lower Cretaceous gives an insight into things to come. The succeeding 30 million years or so (*c.*98 to 65 million years ago) saw the build-up of rocks formed by a succession of blooms of Coccolithophoridae, a group of single celled algae, whose minute calcareous plates (coccoliths) form the bulk of the chalk. This thick, pure limestone is surprisingly widespread, stretching from Australia to Texas, from Ireland to the Donbas and forms the main topographical feature in the Humber area. Not only does it form the scarp feature of the Lincolnshire and Yorkshire Wolds, but its easterly dip ensures that it forms the solid rock below eastern Lincolnshire and Holderness. The last vestige of influence by the Market Weighton Structure is seen in slight

8

thinning of the Lower Chalk in that area. The rock itself is important commercially for it provides a considerable proportion of the water for Hull and the surrounding area, it forms the basis of the whiting and cement industry both north and south of the river, and it forms the firm foundation on which the northern pier of the Humber Bridge is based. It is also the rock in which the buried cliff is cut (see later).

2. The Tertiary Interval

Lasting from 65 to 2 million years ago this is characterised by non-deposition in northern England although many thousands of feet of rock were laid down out in the North Sea. The area was uplifted, tilted gently eastwards and the drainage pattern initiated which started to erode the Mesozoic rocks and carry them eastwards into the proto-North Sea. At this time, the drainage was dominantly east-west and was only subsequently modified along the north-south lines of the Trent and Ouse.

3. Pleistocene Ice Age

During the late Tertiary the climate started to deteriorate and about two million years ago ushered in the start of the Ice Age. Snow and ice building up over high ground in Scandinavia, Scotland and Northern England started to move westwards and southwards. This had two principal effects. First, the ice incorporated material over which it flowed and debris falling on to its surface which, when the ice melted, went to form Boulder Clay and outwash deposits which mantle much of the solid rocks of the area (Fig. 1.2). Second, the presence of ice from the south of Scotland and Scandinavia to the east blocked the natural drainage eastwards and forced changes in the river pattern.

(i) The Boulder Clays

These unsorted clays with their striated pebbles and boulders made up of a wide variety of materials over which the ice passed on its

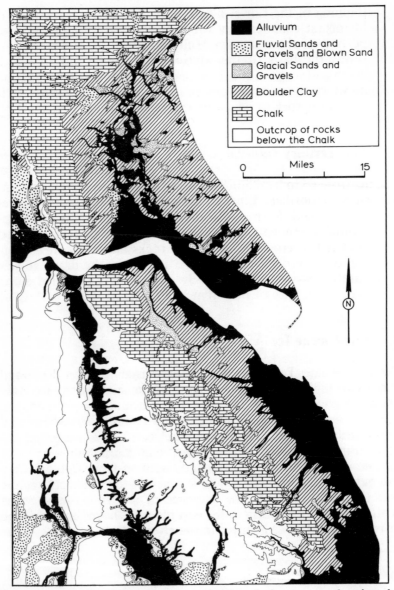

Figure 1.2   Geological map of the Humber drainage area showing the drift and superficial deposits.

travels are the most obvious legacy of glaciation but by no means the only one. The Ice Age was a period of considerable complexity with warmer, interglacial periods alternating with times of intense cold. A simple division may be made into the earlier boulder clays, the 'Older Drift' and the younger 'Newer Drift', separated by a warmer interval known as the Ipswichian Stage.

(a) The Older Drift

These deposits are not extensive in our area, having been subjected to later erosion and dissection, and they are often hidden by the later boulder clays. Their main representatives are the Basement Till of Bridlington Bay and a number of boulder clays, given local names, which occur west of Kirmington and south of Brigg. The Basement Till contains erratics from north-east England, together with a few from Norway, and also incorporates clays with marine fossils picked up in its passage over the North Sea and known as the Bridlington Crag and Sub-Basement Clay.

(b) The Ipswichian Stage

After these early glacial episodes the climate improved to such an extent that hippopotamus, hyaena and other large mammals roamed the area. The accompanying melting of ice caused the sea-level to rise by about 17m and cut a cliff into the Chalk which was subsequently hidden by later boulder clays and is known as the 'Buried Cliff'. This is seen on the coast at Sewerby, just north of Bridlington, where the old beach shingle of that Ipswichian Sea is overlain by rain wash and blown sand. The shingle has yielded straight-tusked elephant, narrow-nosed rhinoceros, spotted hyaena, water vole and unconfirmed hippopotamus. From Sewerby the buried cliff runs inland through Driffield, Beverley and Cottingham to the Humber at Hessle. Seen in the early years of this century in the Station Yard at Hessle, it was beautifully re-exposed in 1984 during the construction of the South Orbital Road. This exposure now no longer exists and the chalk of the cliff provides a solid foundation for one of the bridges connected with the road. South of the river the buried

11

cliff continues down past Kirmington and on through South
Lincolnshire.

(c) The Newer drifts

Some 70,000 years ago the climate again started to deteriorate
ushering in the Devensian Stage which ended 10,000 years
ago. Accumulation of ice with concomitant withdrawal of
water from the sea, reduced sea-level and accelerated erosion
of the older drifts during much of this time. It was not until
late in Devensian time that glaciers re-entered the area about
18,000 years ago and finally disappeared some 5,000 years
later. They left behind the Drab and Purple Tills (now known
as the Skipsea and Withernsea Tills respectively) which are
well exposed along the Holderness coast. These blanket
Holderness and much of east Lincolnshire extending inland a
considerable distance up the dip slope of the Wolds both
north and south of the river. The so-called 'Hessle Till',
originally thought to be the highest boulder clay in the area, is
now known to be simply the weathered top of any of the
underlying tills.

Associated with these boulder clays are melt-water sands
and gravels of which the best known are the Kelsey Hill
Gravels which extend as a low ridge past the villages of
Thorngumbald and Keyingham.

(ii) **The Changes in Drainage Pattern**

As noted earlier, drainage during the Tertiary period was
essentially eastwards, directly to the sea. During the Ice Age this
was fundamentally modified by events outside the immediate area
of the Humber. One of the effects of the Devensian glaciation
responsible for the Newer Drifts was that ice pressed in upon the
East Coast and blocked the eastern exits of the pre-existing
drainage. The result was to pond back the natural drainage and
melt-water from the ice front which then formed a series of lakes
in the North Yorkshire Moors. The history of these was ably described by Kendall in the early years of this century. The lakes
associated with Eskdale and Glaisdale drained to lower and lower

12

levels, eventually spilling out down Newtondale into the Vale of Pickering. Here they found the eastern exit at Filey Bay blocked by ice (and later by a boulder clay plug left by the ice) and the western exit blocked by a glacier occupying the Vale of Mowbray and Vale of York. Thus, hemmed in by ice on two sides, the Jurassic Moors to the north and the Cretaceous Wolds to the south a lake came into existence. Lake Pickering was thus formed and rose until its surface reached a height of 75m O.D. at which point it managed to escape southwards cutting the Kirkham Abbey Gorge in the process. Having made its way southwards into the Vale of York there was still no exit to the sea and in consequence a large body of standing water known as Lake Humber came to occupy the lower parts of the Vale of York and Vale of Trent. It was not until this lake reached a height of 30m O.D. that it managed to flow out through the Humber gap to the North Sea. In doing so it left behind the lacustrine deposits which hide the solid rocks which floor the lower part of the Vale of York, and the marginal gravels which are found in places along the western edge of the Vale and round Holme upon Spalding Moor at heights of about 30m O.D. Evidence of the glacier blocking the northern end of the Vale of York at this time is seen in the moraines left behind when the ice melted. A southern one representing one period of standstill of the glacier is named after the village of Escrick and is seen particularly well at Wilberfoss. A second period of standstill and melting is seen in the York Moraine, on which the city stands.

Meanwhile, after the disappearance of the ice, the deposits left behind continued to ensure that the drainage followed its new course with the result that streams near Robin Hood's Bay which once flowed a mere 8km eastward to the sea, now drain into the Derwent and follow a circuitous course of more than 140 km to reach the sea at Spurn Point.

4. Subsequent History

The disappearance of the ice was followed by gradual amelioration of climate from tundra to cool temperate with increase in the amount of birch afforestation. This culminated just before the Flandrian in a regression to cold conditions with a considerable development of solifluction and, in the drier areas, blown sand.

The latter is found covering some of the Jurassic rocks at the southern end of the Vale of York and near Scunthorpe. The last 10,000 years belong to the Flandrian Stage or Holocene and show the continuing evolution of the landscape from the retreat of the ice up to the present day. The irregular surface of the boulder clay allowed the development of shallow lakes or meres in its hollows which usually quickly silted up to form boggy or swampy areas. The largest one remaining is Hornsea Mere. Meanwhile, the improving climate allowed the establishment of larger trees and forests while at the same time ensuring further melting of the ice caps and thus a rise in sea-level. A combination of these two features is seen in the submerged forests of alder, willow, oak, hazel and scotch fir which can be seen from time to time in the Humber Estuary. At the same time, this rise in sea-level flooded much of the low-lying land in Holderness producing a veneer of fine grained silt or warp over the pre-existing deposits and initiating in places the growth of peat on a large scale.

During this period man has left a number of traces in the area in the form of artefacts such as the Maglemosian harpoon found at Skipsea Withow and the Bronze Age boats found at North Ferriby. The final disappearance of peat bog and drainage of the swampy areas can also be attributed to the work of man in historic times. Meanwhile, as a counter to this reclamation, the sea continually attacks the soft boulder clays of Holderness whose cliffs are retreating on average some 1.5m per year.

Finally, this saga of construction and destruction continues in the cyclical development of Spurn Point whose periodic re-formation at approximately 250 year intervals is documented elsewhere.

Selected Bibliography

Boylan, P.J. 1967. The Pleistocene Mammals of the Sewerby-Hessle buried cliff. *Proc. Yorks. Geol. Soc. 36*, 115-25.

Catt, J.A. and Penny, L.F. 1966. The Pleistocene deposits of Holderness, East Yorkshire. *Proc. Yorks. Geol. Soc., 35* 375-420.

De Boer, G. 1963. Spurn Point and its predecessors. *Naturalist*, 113-20.

De Boer, G. 1964. Spurn Head: its history and evolution. *Trans Inst. Br. Geogr.* No. *34*, 71-89.

De Boer, G., Neale, J.W., and Penny, L.F. 1958. A guide to the geology of the area between Market Weighton and the Humber. *Proc. Yorks. Geol. Soc., 31*, 157-209.

Kendall, P.F. 1902. A system of glacier lakes in the Cleveland Hills. *Q.Jl. Geol. Soc. Lond., 58*, 471-571.

Kent, P.E. 1980. Eastern England from the Tees to the Wash. *British Regional Geology H.M.S.O.*, 155 pp.

Penny, L.F. and Catt, J.A. 1967. Stone orientation and other structural features of tills in East Yorkshire. *Geol. Mag.*, 104, 344-60.

Rayner, D.H. and Hemingway, J.E. (Eds.) 1974. *The Geology and Mineral Resources of Yorkshire*. 405 pp. W.S. Maney and Son Ltd., Leeds.

Swinnerton, H.H. and Kent, P.E. 1976. The Geology of Lincolnshire. *Lincs. Nat. Union, Lincs. Nat. Hist. Brochure* No. 7, 130 pp.

II

History of the Humber coastline

G. de Boer

Introduction

1. The upper Humber system

   (i)   The Ouse and Trent tidal plain
   (ii) The upper Humber

2. The lower Humber

Introduction

There has been much artificial modification of the Humber shores
from medieval times to the present day — embanking, draining,
reclamation and warping. Many of these changes can be traced on
the relevant sheets of the Ordnance Survey 1:50,000 maps (sheets
106, 107, 112, 113), and map references will be given to them
throughout this chapter.

The need, opportunities, and scope for such modifications were
very largely consequences of the physical history of the Humber
and its headstreams and tributaries after the last glacial period, the
Devensian. When the Devensian ice melted away, sea-level was
low at first and the Humber and its tributary rivers and streams cut
down their valleys to depths of 25m or more below sea-level.
During the following rise of sea-level to present day heights, which
were not approached until about 5000 years ago, these deeply cut
valleys were first flooded and then silted up in their lower reaches
to produce tracts of flat, ill-drained estuarine silt or warp, and

16

stretches of peat fen or carrland in their obstructed upper courses. This rise of sea-level, which still continues, though more slowly, is also an important contributory factor to the notoriously rapid erosion of the Holderness coast which causes changes at the mouth of the Humber. The changes in the estuary will be described from the head of the Humber to its mouth. The name Humber belongs only to the 60km (37 miles) of estuary from the confluence of Ouse and Trent at Trent Falls (SE 8623) to the sea. At Trent Falls a triangle of training walls, built about 1920, guides the waters of the two confluent rivers into each other but in medieval times the confluence was more complex and this makes necessary some account of the changes in the river courses across the wide, flat plain surrounding the head of the Humber.

1.   The upper Humber system

(i)   The Ouse and Trent tidal plain

Except where they appear as the low mounds of the Isle of Axholme and Crowle Hill (SE 780133), the reddish Triassic marls underlying this plain are below sea-level and buried beneath the clays and sands dropped by melt water from glaciers and by the clays and silts, or suspended material (locally known as 'warp') left by the tides of the Humber when sea-level rose after the ice had melted away (Fig. 2.1). Forests which had flourished before the rise of sea-level were overwhelmed, buried and turned to beds of peat. The high tides of the Humber held back the rivers, especially their water flows, causing flooding and waterlogging. Sphagnum moss flourished and developed into some of the biggest raised peat bogs in England and Wales, Thorne Waste (SE 7215) and Hatfield Moors (SE7006). Across this waste the Don, Torne, and Idle coiled and twisted in interlaced courses. The silt-laden tides coming up these rivers deposited more warp on their banks than further into the plain when they flooded, and so built up natural embankments or levees alongside the rivers.

  The stages by which this region of isle, marsh flat, and peat bog, lying below high spring tide level, was brought to its present state can be traced on the Ordnance Survey maps (sheets 106, 112). Of the medieval landscape there is left the pattern of village settlement

17

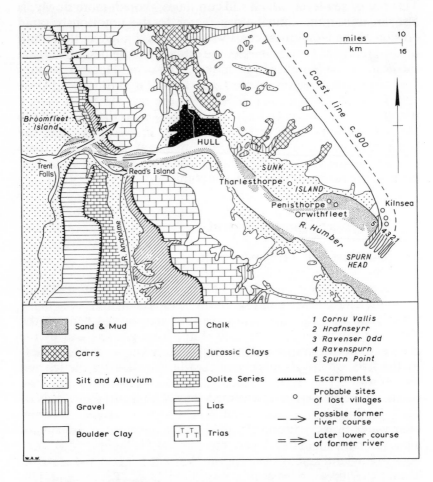

Figure 2.1   The Humber: geology, coastline and early settlements.

and the vestiges of the old river courses. Belton (SE 755068) and Crowle (SE 7713) are on the natural islands, the other villages on natural levees artifically raised and strengthened on the banks of the Ouse or the Trent or marking the former course of the Don from near Crowle (SE 755126) through Eastoft, Luddington, Fockerby, Garthorpe, and Adlingfleet to the Trent so that Trent Falls was virtually a triple confluence. Medieval man found it easier to keep the tide out than the rivers in, and for much of the year flood water regularly spread over the low ground round these island sites and formed great sheets of water covering thousands of acres.

What medieval man could not do was achieved by Cornelius Vermuyden between 1626 and 1629, by giving each river a more direct course to its own outlet. His New River Idle reaches the Trent at West Stockwith (SK 790947) a little north of Gainsborough. The Torne (SE 764080) he led in a straightened channel northwards and eastwards to the Trent at Althorpe (SE 832095). Dutch River (SE 710213), into which he turned the lower Don, was a second thought, his first diversion of it northwards into the Ouse higher up near East Cowick (SE 669228) having been unsuccessful.

The next major step consisted of warping and improved drainage. Warping was possible because the area is below high tide level. It helped drainage because the accumulation of warp raised the lowest lying areas and it transformed land values by giving, in three or four years, nearly worthless areas of poor peaty ground a covering of first class fertility. Warping was described by Arthur Young in 1799 as follows:

> The water of the tides that come up the Trent, Ouse, Don, and other rivers, which empty themselves into the great estuary of the Humber, is muddy to an excess; insomuch that in summer if a cylindrical glass 12 or 15 inches long be filled with it, it will presently deposit an inch, and sometimes more, of what is called warp . . . The improvement is perfectly simple and consists of nothing more than letting in the tide at high water to deposit the warp, and permitting it to run off again as the tide falls . . . the mud is not to manure the soil, but to create it.

Warping was a specific remedy for both the ills the area suffered — poor soils and low levels. Most was done between 1800 and

1860, and by the latter year virtually all the peat lands within three miles (5km) of the Trent from the Ouse to the Isle of Axholme had been warped, transforming very poor soil into potentially excellent land, if properly drained. A description of 1851 provides a sharply engraved vignette of the area then — 'an immense plain . . . dark arable fields, intersected by long lines of drains, and exhibiting bright shining spaces where distant warping works are in progress'.

When warping was finished, the warping drains served as ordinary drains. Since then there have been further improvements to drainage, and pumping stations have been built to lift water from the main drains into the tidal rivers, e.g. at Keadby (SE 835113).

(ii) The upper Humber

The area north of the Ouse and Humber and west of the Yorkshire Wolds has a similar range of conditions and to it have been applied the same remedies of flood banks, draining and warping and, in addition, reclamation from the Humber. As well as being flat, the area is very low-lying, and the numerous occurrences of the place-name elements 'carr' (marsh), '-sea' (pool), 'moor' and 'fen' in the Ordnance Survey maps indicate the former character of these waterlogged sands and clays. The River Foulness meandered into Wallingfen, then probably a shallow lake much of the time for there was only a tidal creek, Skelfleet (SE 897274), east of Broomfleet to let its water out intermittently at low tide. Much of the ground by the Humber was below high spring tide level and a belt of saltmarsh up to 6km wide and subject to regular flooding stretched from the foot of the Wolds westwards. Nevertheless, this was the first part reclaimed. Beginning from further west, banks had been raised on the natural levees by the estuary as far east as Faxfleet (SE 866242) by 1275, Broomfleet by 1304, and further east still later in the fourteenth century. Other inland banks protected the north side of this belt of saltmarsh, and ditches were cut right across it to drain the embanked area. Three such channels had been cut from the River Foulness to the Humber at Blacktoft (SE 842242), Thornton Land (SE 854241), and Faxfleet by 1200, and hamlets such as Greenoak (SE 813279), Bellasize (SE 826278),

20

Bennetland (SE 827288) and Gowthorpe (SE 853253) grew up. Diversion of Foulness water into these channels and into a new cut, Langdike, eastwards across Hotham Carrs (SE 860328), meant that by 1300 the carrs could be used for summer pasture and peat cutting. By 1425 the common pasture south of Langdike was called Wallingfen Common and a court of forty-eight jurymen (SE 850297), one from each of the villages concerned, regulated its use. The names Weighton Common (SE 8640), Holme Common, Cliff Common signify the sharing between these villages of the carrs north of Langdike by 1456.

In 1690 a shift of channel moved the Humber away from its bank which before ran in an arc from Brough across Mill Beck at SE 910283 and by the sites of Providence Farm (SE 890279) and Weighton Lock (SE 874257), and the salt-marsh which had accreted here on Ellerker Sands and adjacent areas was embanked in 1706.

Despite some improvement, Wallingfen remained summer pasture flooded for three to ten months of the year, with some permanent meres, e.g. Oxmarrdyke Marr (SE 8528). The Market Weighton Canal, 1772-82, attempted to provide both drainage and navigation, functions not easily combined, for the one requires a low water level, the other a high. Though not fully effective as a drain, the canal helped, as a description of 1856 testifies: 'The vast commons of Walling Fen and Bishopsoil (further west), containing upwards of 9,000 acres (3,600ha), which, fifty or sixty years ago, were a dreary waste, full of swamps and broken grounds, and which in foggy or stormy weather could not be crossed without danger, are now covered with well built farmhouses, and intersected with good roads'.

Cessation of navigation, partial in 1900, but not complete until 1958, has allowed the canal to be fully effective as a drain; the upper part has been emptied.

The enrichment of soil by warping has been carried on here since the late eighteenth century. Warping drains were cut near Blacktoft and Yokefleet to carry silt-laden water up to 5km inland into embanked fields, where it was held by sluices until the silt settled. It was last carried out about 1950.

There was further reclamation near Broomfleet. An island appeared to the east, was embanked by 1846, washed away soon after, reappeared in 1853, and 60 acres (24ha) were embanked by

21

1870. By 1900 the channel round it, Broomfleet Hope (SE 890270) was dry, and it and the now bigger island, 600 acres (240ha) together, were embanked in 1907.

The Ancholme Valley on the south bank (Fig. 2.1) was hollowed out of the upper Jurassic clays between the Lincolnshire limestone ridge and the Lincolnshire Wolds when early late-glacial sea-levels were low, and the forest that grew there turned into peat bog when higher sea-levels flooded it and deposited a layer of silt. The main steps in the improvement of the valley can be seen on the Ordnance Survey map. The medieval condition of a sluggish, choked, meandering river regularly flooding is suggested by the bordering lines of villages, drawn back on each side to rising ground, and the word 'carr' (marsh) everywhere. The mouth was embanked against the Humber. Sir John Munson's rectification of the river course by his cutting of the New River Ancholme in 1635-9, which intersects the meanders of the old river, and his making of a Ferriby Sluice to keep out the tide, came next. The insufficiencies of these measures and the effects of opposition and neglect were to some extent repaired by an entrance lock and new sluice in the eighteenth century; the New River had to serve the mutually antagonistic functions of drainage and navigation. A further step to remedy the continued flooding was the making of catchwater drains to take upland water to separate sluices from 1825 on. There have been further measures taken in the present century by lowering water levels in the river and installing pumps.

There is an area of reclamation from the bed of the Humber itself just off Ferriby Sluice, Read's Island (SE 965220), which is a patch of salt-marsh that grew on what was Ferriby Sands. In 1841, the Read family of Burton on Stather (SE 865185) leased it from the Crown and embanked 75 acres (30ha) which by 1886 had become 450 acres (80ha); about one third has been lost since by erosion. In the Humber Gap where the estuary cuts through the chalk escarpment of the Yorkshire and Lincolnshire Wolds, there have been no very large changes of the Humber shore, but below the gap the changes have been very considerable, especially on the north side.

2. The lower Humber

Between the Yorkshire Wolds and Holderness lies, as it were, a moat, a depression flushed out by the melt-water pouring from the edge of the ice sheet that once covered Holderness. The lower Humber fills the south-eastern half of this moat, but the little River Hull fails to fill the northern half and, instead, wanders across peaty carrs between islands of boulder clay and gravel above Beverley and over flats of tidal silt from Beverley to the Humber. Like the Ancholme valley, the Hull valley was deepened when sea-level was low, flooded and filled with peats and silts when the sea rose again, and it suffered the same ponding back of landwater by tidal water, and has similarly gone through a succession of drainage improvements from medieval to modern times.

In medieval times the River Hull was largely empty of settlement except on morainic islands; the remains of Meaux Decoy (TA 080403) recall both the character and one use of this fenland. The monks of the Cistercian Abbey of Meaux (TA 092395), founded in 1150, turned the Lambwath Stream westwards to the Hull, which helped transport more than drainage. The name Engine Drain (TA 087365) records the installation of windmill pumps in 1675, but real improvement only came by turning the water southwards again into the new main drains, mainly after 1763. Even these drains were of limited effect because of Hull's insistence that the water must be taken into the river to keep the port's haven scoured. Only when docks by the Humber had become more important for shipping than the mouth of the Hull was a direct outfall for the Holderness Drain to the Humber made near Marfleet (TA 131286) in 1832. Pumps have been installed here since. All Hull's Humberside docks are on reclaimed foreshore. Unreclaimed foreshore remains where Salt End jetties (TA 156271), constructed 1914-59, by their length give an indication of how, by the construction of these docks, Hull has extended southwards beyond the original shore of the Humber. East of Hull and between the southern edge of the rolling morainic landscapes of Holderness and the Humber lie drained marshes and areas of reclamation, both of Humber silt or warp and both are high-grade farmland. As elsewhere along the Humber, there was early medieval embanking against flood, helped no doubt by a sea-level somewhat lower than at present, and hamlets and large farms or

23

granges, sometimes with moats like Old Little Humber (TA 206236) were put here, probably in the eleventh and twelfth centuries. These siltland farms were areas of early medieval enclosure. Some of this land, for example, was given to Meaux Abbey (TA 0939) and they established a grange here about 1150-60 at Saltaugh — the salt enclosure.

This was not the present Saltaugh Grange (TA 238217) but was situated further south. Just as further east where there is now the reclaimed land of Sunk Island, villages were overwhelmed by tidal inundation (Fig. 2.1), so here also there were great sea floods and erosion from about 1250 onwards, and the abbey chronicle tells how the monks were forced to take all their buildings away from their old Saltaugh Grange and re-erect them at a new Saltaugh Grange further inland where the site survives but not the buildings (Fig. 2.2).

By the late seventeenth century, there was a shoal here, Cherry Cobb Sand, and by the mid-eighteenth century mud had accreted so that it was only covered by water at the highest spring tides (Fig. 2.2). It was so near the shore, and whatever channel there was between it and the mainland was so slight, that sheep could cross easily and graze on the grass which covered it, and it strongly invited reclamation.

The problem was one of ownership. If the land had grown up from the bed of the estuary separated from the shore by a channel (and an older name Cherry Holme (= island) Sand gave colour to this suggestion) then it was Crown land. If it had accreted gradually to the river frontage of the manor of Little Humber, then the Lord of the Manor, William Constable of Burton Constable (TA 190368), had a claim to it. Cherry Cobb Sand stretched from Little Humber to Saltaugh Grange and the then owners, the charitable Corporation of the Sons of the Clergy, established to relieve widows and orphans of clergymen, wanted a share in the new land. With the support of the Crown, they brought an action against Constable in 1763, but he won the case. One of the issues in the case was the question of whether the North Channel of the Humber which separated Sunk Island from Holderness also separated or, though now warped up, formerly separated Cherry Cobb Sand likewise. It seems that it was argued successfully that the channel lay instead between Cherry Cobb Sand and Foulholme Sand (TA 2021). To pre-empt further

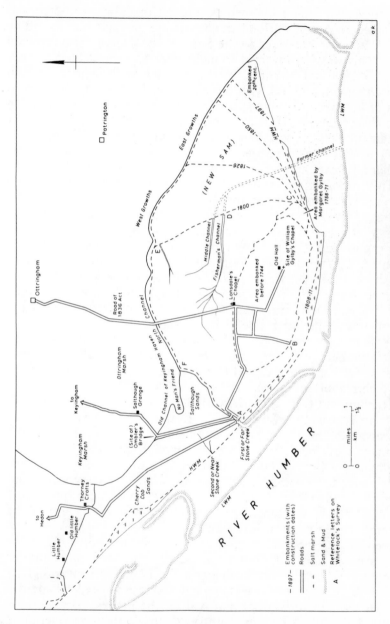

Figure 2.2   The stages of reclamation of Sunk Island.

25

litigation and secure his own position, Constable promoted and obtained an Act of Parliament authorising the reclamation and by which he gave 400 acres to the Sons of the Clergy for a nominal rent. This was the inverted triangle with its apex at Stone Creek (TA 236190) and bounded by the two drains, Keyingham Drain and Ottringham Drain with outlets there. In this way the eastern end of his own area now shut the Saltaugh Grange land off from any river frontage, thus avoiding a repetition of the situation if reclamation of Foulholme Sands became practicable. In fact, though this was considered, it was never carried out. The embanking of Cherry Cobb Sands was completed in 1770.

This reclamation (and that of Sunk Island also) led to the progressive silting up of the North Channel and to a general aggravation of the drainage problems of the older Holderness marsh lands. These were remedied by the cutting of Thorngumbald Drain (TA 180250) in 1776 emptying into the Humber upstream of the Sand, and the making of a new, more direct outlet for Keyingham Drain at Stone Creek in 1802. The former course with its reversed S-bend (TA 240205), which significantly used to have the name No Man's Friend, used to wind eastwards round the north side of Sunk Island. Where Sunk Island is now, in early medieval times there was a broad strip of lowland by the Humber with several villages such as Tharlesthorpe, Frismersk, Penisthorpe, and Orwithfleet. Tharlesthorpe seems to have been south of Ottringham at about TA 2720; the other places lay further east (Fig. 2.2). Between about 1250 and 1400 their land was progressively overwhelmed. Despite the throwing up of successive defence lines of embankment, the land was lost and the Humber bank now ran from near Saltaugh Grange (TA 239216) through Patrington Haven (TA 3021). In due course shoals accumulated, one especially near to where Tharlesthorpe had been. It is called Sunk Sand on the first map in which it appears (of about 1560). It was separated from Holderness by an arm of the Humber called the North Channel.

Step by step the sand became ready for reclamation — '. . . at first a great bank of sand . . . thereat mud and other matter stopt, and then still more by degrees. The island when it was given to Col. A.G. was never overflown but at spring tides. At neap tides . . . it was constantly dry and had on the highest parts thereof grass.' This Col. A.G. was Anthony Gylby, a Royalist veteran of the Civil War who came to Hull after the Restoration, and was MP for the town along with Andrew Marvell. As an island growing up from the bed of a tidal river, it was crown land, and Gylby was granted a lease for 99 years from 1675 and embanked about 20 acres (8ha). His grandson and successor as leasee, William Gylby, extended the reclaimed area to about 1560 acres (640ha) by 1711, established farms, and built a chapel near the Old Hall (TA 278177).

The next major intake was not made until the turn of the eighteenth century, but it was the largest single addition in the history of the island, 2700 acres (1080ha), and by extending the reclaimed area west to Stone Creek (TA 236189) and north to the North Channel, it virtually joined it to the mainland (Fig. 2.2). Further additions have been made at the eastern end of the island, continuing into the present century, and some of the stages and kind of landscape are reflected in names such as East Bank Farm (TA 294178), Bleak House Farm (TA 204199), Newlands (TA 313176) and Outstray Farm (TA 323194). The later reclamations were undertaken by the Commissioners of Crown Lands and the farms and cottages they built on their intakes of the 1850s have ornamental plaques above their doors with V.R., a crown and a date.

Sea coast and estuary shore converge to make south-eastern Holderness a wedge of land from the end of which Spurn Head curves south-westwards into the mouth of the Humber and thereby gains shelter from the northerly gales. This shelter, by shouldering off the more destructive waves, has allowed flatter, more constructive waves to build a small proportion of the spoil from the Holderness coast into this long finger of beach and sand dune that pokes nearly halfway across the mouth of the estuary.

Because Spurn grows out from a coast that is ever falling back, it has had always to adjust itself to this retreat, and because it has a strategic position at the mouth of a major estuary, as the presence there of a lighthouse, and lifeboat, pilot, and coastguard stations bear witness, there is an unusual length of historical record which registers these adjustments. It seems that as the coast retreats, Spurn loses the shelter it needs for its existence, so that about every 250 years it is breached by waves, the far end washed away, and a new spit grows inside the position of its predecessor. It is presently about 5½km long, probably longer than it has been before (Fig.

2.1).

The present spit, perhaps the fifth recorded, began to develop after its predecessor was breached and washed away about 1608, and its subsequent history can be traced in some detail from the succession of lighthouses built here from 1673 on and from maps, surveys, and records of litigation (Fig. 2.3). A storm opened a great breach in 1849, and soon Spurn was but a string of islets at high water, probably shortly to be washed away, had not the breaches been closed and groynes installed whereby it has survived for 379 years compared with the 250 year span of its predecessors. It is now very vulnerable as the breaking of a stretch of road near the northern end in January, 1978, and further inundations in the following December and in February 1983 showed.

The earliest record tells of a hermit establishing a cell here in the seventh century. A Scandinavian adventurer was wrecked here *c*. 950 on what was probably the next spit, Ravenser, meaning Raven's sand bank, whence sailed the army defeated at Stamford Bridge in 1066. On its successor, Ravenser Odd (the headland near Ravenser), flourished the port of that name until both were swept away by the sea about 1360. Ravenser Spurn, the fourth spit, where Henry Bolingbroke met a hermit when he landed in 1399, where another hermit began to build a lighthouse in 1427, and where Edward IV came ashore in 1471 to recover his kingdom, lasted until 1608.

The south side of the Humber was also a marshland, similar to the north, protected from high tides by an embankment, but was not rated as highly as farmland and a good deal of it was used for grazing cattle.

Danish settlers possibly as early as 866 found a useful tidal creek reaching back from the Humber to low mounds of boulder clay rising above the coastal marshes and Grimsby grew here at the head of its haven. The haven was fairly small and some use was made of the mouth of the River Freshney until, in the fourteenth century, part of the flow of the Freshney was diverted to the original haven. Later the port languished however, until in 1800, the Freshney was diverted completely into the haven. It was deepened, widened, and lockgates made it a dock, the Old Dock. The Royal Dock was built between 1848 and 1852 on reclaimed foreshore and gave Grimsby its characteristic shape on the map — its jut into the Humber. The recess immediately upstream of this

28

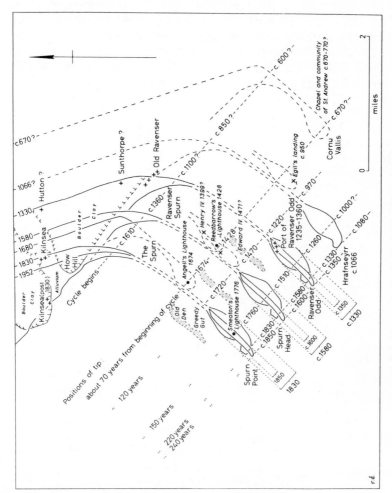

Figure 2.3 The history of Spurn Point.

project is the site of a recent reclamation proposal. The first fish dock opened in 1857 on more reclaimed foreshore just east of the Royal Dock.

East of Grimsby and the mud flats of the Humber there used to be a short stretch of coast with Holderness conditions, eroding boulder cliffs (the last north of the Wash), yielding sand to form beaches, and the hamlet of Cleethorpes here became a fashionable resort for sea-bathing in the early nineteenth century. The boulder clay cliffs and hills are now protected from erosion by a sea wall and concealed under a promenade and gardens.

III

The physical characteristics of the Humber

J.S. Pethick

Introduction

1. History of the Humber

2. Tides

3. Sediments

4. The future

Introduction

The Humber Estuary is one of the most important and well-known estuaries of the world. In size, of course, it cannot compare with giants such as the estuary of the Rio de la Plata (compare the scales in Fig. 3.1) which is 2000km wide at its mouth and boasts a tidal length of 500km. In comparison to this the width of the Humber is insignificant — a mere 15km, and its tidal length — 120km — will fit into the width of la Plata with room to spare. Yet what the Humber lacks in quantity it makes up for in quality. For one thing the large estuaries of the world are too big to be encompassed by the eye of the shore-bound observer. The opposite banks of la Plata, Brahmaputra or Amazon are made invisible by the curvature of the earth, but the opposite bank of the Humber mouth, on the proverbial clear day, can just be made out. Thus the Humber is exactly the right size for observation, an important

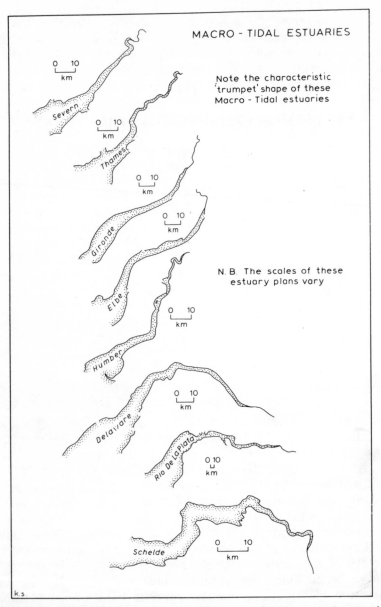

Figure 3.1 The shape of the Humber in relation to other major estuaries.

point in its favour; it has, however, another attraction for the *cognescenti* of estuaries — its shape. The classic estuary outline has often been described as trumpet-shaped, and the Humber, as can be seen in Fig. 3.1 is an excellent example of this. Perhaps a better description might be saxophone-shaped due to the marked bend east of the River Hull, a bend which will be discussed more fully later in this chapter. Fig. 3.1 illustrates the remarkable similarity between the Humber and many other estuaries of the world and it is this very fact, that it is not different, but entirely representative, that makes it so interesting to scientists.

At this point it is as well to pause to consider what we mean by the word 'estuary'. Many attempts at definition have been made. 'A drowned river valley', 'the tidal mouth of a river', or, more tediously, 'a semi-enclosed body of water which has a free connection with the sea and in which sea water is measurably diluted with fresh water'. All of these are true but are rather like the descriptions of the elephant made by the blind Indians — none sum up the totality of the animal. Indeed, the surest way to understand what constitutes an elephant or an estuary is to see for yourself. This is why the observable size of the Humber and its representative shape are so important — we can see for ourselves what an estuary is. Here, however, a note of caution should be sounded, for the Humber is a splendid example of an estuary with a large tidal range (more than 4m). It is not comparable with estuaries, such as the Exe Estuary in Devon, which have a medium tidal range (2-4m), or those in seas with small tides (less than 2m) such as the Mediterranean (the mouth of the Rhône for example) or the Gulf of Mexico (the Mississippi). These estuaries tend to be short and stubby or infilled with a delta and are not to be compared with the elegant flare of the Humber.

1. History of the Humber

The history of the Humber, like that of any part of our landscape, is best summed up in the words of Playfair: 'No vestige of a beginning, no prospect of an end'; thus it is difficult to know where to begin. There is some evidence that the Humber once took a more northerly course to the sea but the traces have all but been obscured. Most of the physical features we see today are the result of the development of the estuary over the past 500,000 years, a period marked in Britain by the last two major glaciations. The history of the estuary and that of the advancing and retreating ice sheets are inseparable. Low temperatures meant that precipitation was as snow which remained on the land surface rather than returned to the sea. Hence the sea-level during the main glacial periods was lowered by a considerable amount — down to 150m below today's sea-level. About 200,000 years ago such a sea-level fall occurred as the result of a major ice advance. The effect on the Humber cannot be adequately described, simply because the estuary ceased to exist. Indeed, since the North Sea is, on average, only 50m deep, such a sea-level fall meant that this too ceased to exist. During this phase, known as the Wolstonian glaciation in Britain, the North Sea was probably a swampy region into which the waters of the Humber, Thames and Rhine flowed before making their way south, through what is now the Straits of Dover. The Humber at this time was a river, rather than an estuary, which cut down into its bed forming a deep channel, a channel now filled with tidal sands and muds. This channel cuts down into glacial till: material derived from glacial periods before the one we are considering at the moment, and at some places, at Immingham for instance, cuts even deeper into the chalk, which underlies Holderness. The deep buried channel does not follow the present course of the estuary, however, but keeps to a more or less straight line from Hessle through what is now Aldborough.

About 120,000 years ago the Wolstonian Glaciation gave way to a warmer, inter-glacial period. This lasted for some 40,000 to 50,000 years and is known in Britain as the Ipswichian Inter-glacial. As temperatures increased, the ice melted and water poured back into the oceans, causing a world-wide rise in sea-level to approximately the level it is today. Approximately, but not exactly, for evidence from Sewerby shows that sea-level at this time was perhaps 2m higher than it is at present. The North Sea was restored and the Humber once more became an estuary. If the coastline of this time is traced around Humberside, however, it is seen that the estuary was quite different in shape from that which we now know. The old cliffline, (now buried beneath subsequent glacial deposits) may be traced from Sewerby, around the eastern flank of the Wolds through Cottingham, (where it is marked by a slight break in slope on the Harland Way Hill) and thence to

34

Hessle (where it was recently well exposed near the station during the A63 road extension scheme). Since the North Sea ended at this line it follows that the Humber Estuary did so too. Thus the estuary at this time was some 40km shorter than it is at present and all the familiar features, the River Hull, Skitter Point and Spurn had not yet come into existence.

After 50,000 years of the existence of this shortened Humber the sea-level fell once more as the next and last glaciation occurred. This, the Devensian glaciation, lasted until 12,000 years ago — almost present day on the time scale we are using here. During this period the Humber again ceased to exist as an estuary, since the North Sea once again dried up. The advancing ice deposited vast amounts of material on its bed, material which now forms the glacial tills of Holderness. As the ice eventually retreated, the sea-level rose once again but not quite to its Ipswichian level. The combination of this 1-2m lower sea-level and the raised land surface caused by the glacial till deposits brought Holderness into being and created a new coastline some 40km east of the Ipswichian coastline. The sea-level rose slowly and did not reach its present level until 6000 years ago; during this time the Humber estuary, as we know it, gradually took shape, sediments were deposited in the old buried channels, sand and shingle were swept in with the encroaching sea and formed our beaches and, probably, Spurn Point. At some stage in this sequence the retreating ice front lay from north-west to south-east from the present position of Spurn. This ice front partially blocked the west-east course of the buried channel of the Humber mentioned above and forced it to take a north-west to south-east route along the ice front. This new route started at the present position of Hull and is the cause of the great bend of Skitter Point, which we said above gave the Humber its 'saxophone' look.

At this time, 6000 years ago, the general shape of the Humber — its width, length and course — were as we know them, but a map of the estuary as it then was would look strange to our eyes. Fig. 3.2 shows such a map; the rising sea-level had drowned the Humber channel and some of the surrounding land so that the estuary outline followed the irregularities of the tills left by the ice. The outline as we know it developed over the next 6000 years, a period in which a rapid smoothing of the estuary bed and banks took place due to the immense amount of sands and muds

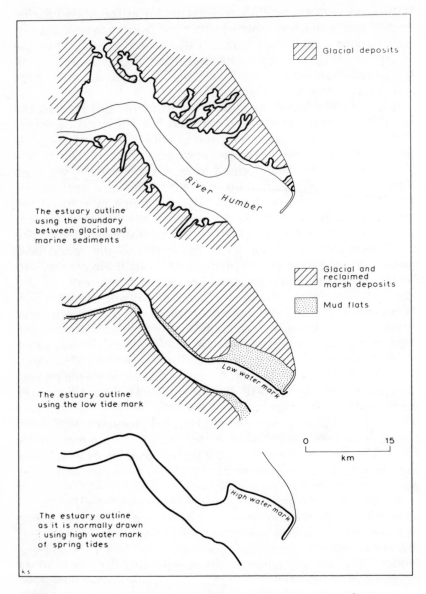

Figure 3.2   The outline of the Humber Estuary, past and present.

deposited by the tides. To understand this modern process we must look briefly at the tidal flows in the Humber.

2. Tides

Most of the modern sediments in the Humber were not derived from the rivers, Trent and Ouse, flowing into the estuary from the uplands, rather they were brought in from the North Sea. The necessary power to transport the many millions of tonnes of mud into the estuary was supplied chiefly by the tides. In their turn, of course, the tides are powered by the gravitational force of the moon and sun, but the Humber and even the North Sea are too small for these forces to have much tide-raising effect. In fact, the tides of the North Sea are powered by Atlantic tides which send a pulse into the northern North Sea each 12.4 hours. This tidal pulse passes down into the North Sea and, as it passes the Humber mouth, a secondary pulse enters the estuary.

It is important to think of the tide, not as the water in a sort of giant bath filled and emptied each twelve hours, but rather as a wave whose surface rises and falls as the water in a bowl would if it were tipped rhythmically, or a wave produced by jerking a long piece of rope. It is difficult to think of the tide as a wave since it appears that the water surface of the estuary is horizontal and rises and falls as water is let into or out of the estuary. This is not so, the water surface is in fact wave-like but the wave is so long, 400km in the mouth of the Humber, and so low, 5-6 metres, that we think of it as a 'water level'. The water within this tidal wave does move, but not as if poured into the estuary from a giant tap. Instead it moves a short distance forward under the wave crest, and then back under the ebb — a circular motion which can be seen on the sea-shore when sea-gulls bob up and down in the waves. As the tidal wave enters the estuary, it encounters a rapidly narrowing channel, consequently the wave edges hit the banks and are bounced back into the oncoming wave. This reflection causes a major change in the tidal water movement, for the currents in the reflected wave are added to the current in the oncoming wave creating a distinct, but to us entirely normal, current regime. First we should imagine what the estuary currents would be like if such reflection did not occur: if, for example, the estuary widened

37

inland instead of narrowing. Let us assume we are standing by the Humber Bridge, as the tidal wave crest approaches from the sea the water level rises and flood tide occurs. But in this non-reflective estuary the currents increase as the water level increases, just as they do, for example in a wave at the sea-shore. Thus at high tide under the Bridge the water would still be moving inland at maximum speed. This is unexpected, but even more startling would be the ebb tide: as the tidal wave crest passes under the Bridge so the water level drops, the water currents, however, would continue to move inland until mid-tide when slack water would occur. At this stage the water would begin to move seaward. That such a current regime does not occur is common observation, but the reasons are hardly ever considered. The explanation is that, as the reflected tidal wave moves back into the incoming wave, the current flows of the two waves are exactly opposite. When the two crests meet, the water level will be at its highest — that is high tide — but the two currents will be opposed and will cancel each other out. The same occurs at low tide; the two wave troughs create a low water level and the opposing currents cancel giving a period of slack or zero current. However, at mid-tide the crest of one of the two waves is coincident with the trough of the other; at this stage both current directions are identical and thus a net current inland on the flood and seawards on the ebb is seen. This is the tidal current regime we are used to, indeed it is difficult to imagine navigation on the Humber if it were otherwise. If currents flowed inland from mid-tide flood until mid-tide ebb then large vessels needing deep water would have to push seaward against the maximum current. Again, if fastest currents were encountered at high tide then deposition of mud along the banks of the estuary would not have taken place, and the rich reclaimed farmland which now borders the estuary would not be there. It is the trumpet-shape of the Humber — that is the rapid narrowing of the channel inland — that causes this reflection of the tidal wave on which so much of our human activity depends, an example of the tightly woven relationships between the various aspects of the estuary which are so characteristic of this environment.

Another facet of the tide which is of vital importance to us is the speed with which it moves. The water within the tidal wave moves quite slowly — 7 or 8 km/hr at the maximum, yet the tidal wave moves very quickly indeed — 50 km/hr at the mouth. Thus, high tide in the estuary is not simultaneous at each point inland, but is achieved in a very rapid sequence. For example, high water at Spurn Point at 5.15 a.m. will be followed by high water at Hessle at 6.15 a.m. : 40km in 1 hour. It is clear from these figures that the tide slows down as it passes inland, the main cause of this is the drag caused by the decrease in the depth of the water. Here, however, another curious fact emerges: since the crest of the tidal wave (high tide) is some 6 or 7 metres higher than the trough (low tide) it follows that the crest is travelling in deeper water than the trough and, because waves move faster in deeper water, should move more quickly. Because of this the tidal crest tends to overtake the trough and thus the wave becomes more and more asymmetrical, with a steep leading edge and a long gentle trailing tail. Since the tide takes 12.4 hours between successive high waters, this asymmetry means that the flood tide (the leading edge of the wave) takes a shorter proportion of this 12.4 hour period as the wave moves inland and consequently the ebb tide (the tail of the wave) takes much longer. At Goole, for instance, the flood tide can take 2 or 3 hours to rise, while the ebb will take 9 or 10 hours to fall. The implications of this on the currents in the channel are extremely important. The rapidly rising flood tide creates strong inland currents while the slowly falling ebb causes much weaker seaward flows. Sediments are, therefore, carried into the estuary on the flood and not removed in the same quantities on the ebb. The estuary has consequently accumulated enormous quantities of mud over the past 6000 years which have smoothed the channel into its trumpet shape and produced the reflected tidal wave with its current regime.

3.   Sediments

We have already noted that most of the sediments in the Humber come in from the North Sea rather than from the rivers. One estimate suggests that 63,400 tonnes of sediment are deposited in the Humber each year, creating, over the past 6000 years, a deposit which varies from 20m to 2m thick. It is not known just how much of this material is derived from river or sea sources. It is known that approximately 200,000 tonnes of sediment are carried into the

Humber each year by river flow, but of course most of this material is merely *en route* for the North Sea. Similarly, it is known that about 1,400,000 tonnes of sediments are contributed to the North Sea from the erosion of Holderness cliffs each year. Here again, however, most of this sediment is moved out into the giant mixing bowl of the southern North Sea and does not enter the Humber, at least not in the short term.

The dominance of sediments derived from the sea seems to be due to the tidal flow asymmetry and the fact that the fresh river water tends to float on the surface of the flow so that its sediments are carried out to sea. Tidal currents are not the only ones which bring sediments into the estuary however; the meeting of the saline sea-water and the fresh river water in the estuary channel creates a second type of current which is of great importance to the amount and position of the sediment concentrations. Since the saline sea-water moving into the estuary with the tide is denser than the fresh river water, the freshwater 'floats' on the surface. The speed of the two flows in the Humber causes the two water masses to mix at the junction between them. Sea-water passes up into the freshwater and is carried out to sea as a surface flow. This removal of sea-water from the bottom-flowing tidal stream is compensated for by more sea-water flowing into the estuary. This extra water sets up a current which is in addition to the tidal current and which moves inland on the bottom of the estuary carrying sediments with it. The limit of the salinity gradient which creates this current lies at about the position of the Humber Bridge, and, since the current flows up to this point, so sediments are brought inland to here, where they tend to concentrate. For this reason the Hessle-Brough section of the estuary has much higher sediment concentrations than other sections of the channel and it may be this fact that accounts for the tendency of the channel shape at this point to fluctuate markedly. For instance the width of the estuary at this point between 1851 and 1966 varied from +30% to −30% of its average, compared with a general 10% to 15% decrease in width for the channel seawards of this reach. This high sediment concentration and consequent rapid deposition rates along the Hessle reach, may be the reason for the pronounced channel swings landward of the Bridge which take the deep water sometimes south of Read's Island, sometimes north. The effects of such channel changes may be seen on the north bank of the Humber west of the Bridge, where erosion has left a 2 metre high cliff in a salt-marsh which once extended without a break on to the mudflats.

The range of sediment types in the Humber is much greater than is generally imagined. The estuary is usually considered to be a muddy river, an impression created by the chocolate waters and the miles of mudflats exposed at low tide. Our impressions are, however, governed by our shore-bound vantage point. If we were able to view the sediments of the Humber from the centre of the channel we would get a very different impression. Fig. 3.3 shows that the central channel sediments are not muddy at all, but composed of sands and even gravels. Although the map appears to be quite complex, in fact there is an underlying simplicity. Basically sediments get finer — that is muddier — towards the banks of the estuary. The reason for this is also straightforward. Coarser sediments, sands and gravels, can only be moved by strong currents, but it is only in the central channel that such speeds are attained and therefore the sand and gravel deposits of the Humber are all found here. As we saw earlier, high tide in the estuary is marked by very slow currents, so that only the very finest material can be moved up on to the channel banks. This creates the large mudflat areas, such as Spurn Bight, which lie between mid- and high tide. An interesting exception to this pattern in Spurn Bight may be seen on the map as a narrow semi-circular strip of sand running just below the high tide mark. This sandy material cutting across an otherwise extremely muddy inter-tidal area, is caused by an eddy current which swirls around the Bight in a clockwise direction from Hawkins Point, on both flood and ebb tides. Although this current cannot easily be detected as a water movement it is perfectly obvious on the sediment map and provides a good example of the close relationship between current and sediment particle size.

It is also interesting to note on the map that the central channel sediments are arranged in linear formation, clearly following the line of the current direction. Between Grimsby and Salt End however, it can be seen that two lines of coarse sediment exist, separated by finer sands. These two deposits mark the course of the flow on the flood and the ebb tides which are quite distinct in this section of the estuary. During the flood the current follows the central channel known as the White Booth Roads, but on the ebb the flow is towards the sides of the channel and runs strongly to

41

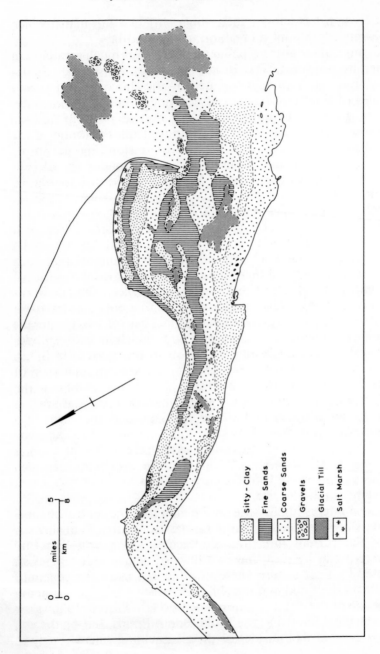

Figure 3.3   The sediments of the Humber Estuary.

the north of the Foulholme spit. The reason for such a difference in tidal flows is that maximum current speed on flood and ebb are attained at quite distinct water depths. On the flood-tide the highest speeds are reached just after mid-tide in this reach of the estuary and quickly drop again, whereas the ebb tide flows strongly just after the turn of the tide and continues to do so for two or three hours. Thus the flood-tide currents tend to be concentrated in a mid-tide channel while the ebb-tide flows through much wider channel sections, a feature which has great importance to navigation in the estuary as well as the influence on bottom sediments shown on the map.

4. The Future

The Humber may appear to us to be a significant and permanent feature on the map of England but, as we have seen, this permanence is a matter of the time-scale we adopt. For us, mere mortals living for a short seventy years, the estuary is indeed a permanent feature, but over a time-scale measured in thousands rather than tens of years this is no longer true. The most obvious change which seems bound to overtake the estuary is that the Holderness coastal erosion will quickly push the mouth westward until it once more reaches the old coastline on the edge of the Wolds. This should take a mere 16,000 years or so — emphasising the transience of the extension of the estuary added just after the last glaciation, and certainly making a major change in the map of England. Less certain, but quite probable, is the arrival of another glacial period which may modify the estuary, just as the previous ones did.

But these changes, however fundamental, do not really concern us; we must be interested in the short-term changes in the estuary. Several can be predicted. First the process of sediment deposition will continue to decrease the width and depth of the channel. A 15% decrease in width of the estuary east of the bridge was noted above, and there seems no reason why such a rate of infill should not continue. Of course such deposition cannot continue indefinitely, the estuary will never be entirely filled up with mud since both tidal and river flows will become more concentrated and serve to keep the channel open. Other inevitable changes will be brought about by the rising sea-level on this coast. At present this rise is in the region of 1-2mm a year and its effects may be seen by anyone crossing the Myton Bridge in Hull and looking south to the Humber Tidal Barrier, built to protect the City of Hull from the increasingly high tides. A 1 or 2mm vertical rise in sea-level can mean a horizontal incursion of 0.5m or so a year across some of the flat lands bordering the estuary. This of course means erosion of the banks and it will be interesting to see whether infill or erosion wins the battle for the channel width.

Inevitably, any discussion of the future of the Humber must include some consideration of Spurn. Its present precarious position has been the subject of many alarmist reports: if it is breached will the currents of the Humber change? Will navigation on the Humber continue? Will the Humber mouth be blocked by the sand eroded from the break-through. . . and so on. A glance at the map of the outer Humber will show that the mouth of the estuary is not defined by Spurn but by the extensive mudflats known as Spurn Bight. It seems likely that Spurn Point was formed as a sand and shingle ridge rolled inland by the rising sea-level after the last glaciation and coming to rest eventually on the mudflats of the Bight. As the Holderness coast erodes so the mouth of the estuary moves inland and Spurn Point moves with it, rolled over on the outer mudflats by the waves. Historical records show that occasionally the spit does break through during this process, but more important, they also show that Spurn has been in position for most of historical times and therefore, it may reasonably be assumed, ever since our present estuary was formed — 6000 years ago. In the short term then, it may be that a breach will occur as it has done in the past, but much more important is the question of the stability of Spurn Bight. If a break through occurs will the mudflats be eroded and disappear?

We have already seen that the Humber has developed a smooth trumpet shape over the past 6000 years as a result of continued deposition. We also saw that this shape controlled the currents in the estuary and that, in turn, the currents formed the shape. This interdependence is characteristic of estuaries and means that shape and process cannot be divorced. The shape of the outer estuary — that is from Hull to the sea — is largely controlled by the infill of Spurn Bight, which has resulted in a stable shape for the estuary as a whole. This infill lies below high tide and continues seaward of

Spurn Point forming the Binks which project 5km into the North Sea, the whole feature forming a 15km long, 5km wide platform which is an integral part of the estuary. Without a major change in the currents or tides of the estuary, which seems unlikely over the next few thousand years, it is as improbable for the mass of Spurn Bight to be removed as it would be for the estuary to take a new course to the sea. Spurn Point itself plays no part in this major relationship between estuary shape and process. Lying above high tide it represents an important feature to shore-bound observers but is quite irrelevant to the mechanics of the estuary. It is clear that, although Spurn Point depends on this massive infill for its existence, the stability of Spurn Bight does not depend on the thin sand veneer of the Point.

All this is of little comfort, of course, to the essential services which depend on Spurn Point — the lifeboat and the lighthouse. A break through of the spit may not be a disaster for the estuary but it would be for these important functions. The road to the Point may be kept open by massive engineering works but the gradual westward movement of the spit must mean that eventually the lighthouse will be left standing in the North Sea.

IV

Life in the Humber

(A)   Salt-marshes

W. Armstrong

Introduction

1.   Marsh development

2.   Succession

3.   Factors affecting the succession

4.   Regression

5.   Primary production, nutrient balance and energy flow

6.   Conservation

Introduction

Salt-marshes are a feature of sheltered shore-lines in many parts of Britain and some of the finest are to be found on the East coast from the Humber estuary southwards. Within the Humber they have a scattered distribution stretching from the mouth at Spurn and at Donna Nook, to as far west as Trent Falls 62km from the sea. Many of the British salt-marshes have been modified by cattle grazing but the particularly fine example illustrated in Plate 1 — Welwick Marsh — is an ungrazed marsh. The photograph highlights two of the most characteristic features of salt-marshes: the zoned (and in places mosaic) distribution of the vegetation, and the presence of deep drainage channels, the creeks, which form a tree-like network across the marsh. A third physiographic feature not evident in the photograph and indeed relatively scarce at Welwick is the salt-pan, the marsh equivalent of the rock-pool — depressions in the marsh often permanently flooded and bare of terrestrial vegetation because of the accumulation of excessive quantities of salts. In ecophysiological terms the zonation of the plants reflects their different tolerances, preferences, and competitiveness in a regime in which wave-action, salinity, submergence, waterlogging and drainage varies both topographically and temporally. Indeed the estuarine marsh is among the most varied of wetland ecosystems. Only the very highest of the spring tides cover the vegetation at the rear of the marsh and these occur only at the spring and autumn equinoxes; sites at the front of the marsh are of much lower elevation and receive at least 360 floodings a year. In between these two extremes the fortnightly springs and fortnightly neap tides provide a considerable range of conditions, mediated by slope and proximity to creeks. Areas close to creeks will drain relatively quickly; more remote sites may remain flooded or waterlogged for considerable periods.

1. Marsh Development

Coastal marshes are the product of sediment accretion and higher-plant establishment and growth. Provided that the nature of the coastline affords adequate protection from the full destructive energies of wave-action, marsh development begins if there is sufficient sediment accretion above the mean high water level of the neap tides (MHWN). Below this level the periods of exposure are insufficiently long for the germination and establishment of colonising species. Colonisation of the exposed mud/sand flats aids accretion, and stabilisation and the coalescing of islands of primary colonisers to form a sward, can accelerate sedimentation and cause a relatively rapid elevation of the land surface. The more elevated the ground, however, the less frequent and of shorter duration are the tidal effects: the accretion rate is slowed, drainage effects become more pronounced and widespread, and the fresh water influxes from rainfall and elsewhere more influential. Rates of accretion and marsh development vary enormously according to location and the photographs in Plate 2 testify to the rapid growth of marsh which can take place in the Humber estuary given favourable conditions. This marsh at the neck of Spurn has developed from bare mud to its present two-community status in about 25 years and now stretches for a distance of some 200m from the original shore-line.

2. Succession

Plant succession on British salt-marshes varies from place to place according to substratum type, climate and other factors. Although it has not always been so, the major colonising species on the Humber and elsewhere at the present time is the sea cord-grass (*Spartina anglica*) (Plate 3), a very vigorous species whose origin and geographical spread are of some interest. It arose first ca. 1870 at a location near Hythe in Southampton Water, as a natural but sterile hybrid (*Spartina x townsendii*) between an alien — *Spartina alterniflora* (the dominant lower marsh grass throughout much of north America) — and our native *Spartina maritima* (a relative rarity). Subsequently, the chromosome number became doubled conferring fertility and this species spread rapidly to both east and west coasts of Britain. Its vigour has led to the development of much new marsh and the extension and modification of existing marshes. Plantings of *S.anglica* in the Humber are known to have taken place and have clearly helped to cause the enlargement of existing marshes and a spread of marsh along the banks of the estuary. The marsh in Plate 2 arose as a direct result of the natural spread of *Spartina*.

The zonations at Welwick marsh are fairly typical of the east coast successions and will be used here as an example of what we expect to find in such a salt-marsh. The lowest reaches are dominated by *S.anglica* which forms a wide sward. Species associated with it but of much lower frequency include the annuals *Salicornia europea* (Plate 3) (glasswort) and *Suaeda maritima* (herbaceous sea-blite). Slight elevations of the mud surface are occasionally topped by tufts of sea poa (*Puccinellia maritima*). Glasswort is very palatable if pickled and is something of a local delicacy on the south bank. Before the arrival of *Spartina*, the *Salicornia* and *Puccinellia* were probably the primary colonisers in the Humber.

The steepest incline on the marsh is to be found immediately to the rear of the *Spartina* belt and is associated with the spread of *Puccinellia* which finally coalesces to form an almost pure and dense sward. *Puccinellia* is a relatively fine-leafed and stoloniferous grass which is very efficient sediment trapper. The main species to co-exist with the *Puccinellia* is the sea aster (*Aster tripolium*) a plant with flowers resembling the Michaelmas Daisy; a variant lacking the purple ray florets is also common.

The creeks also become a very obvious feature at this level for with the establishment of vegetation they become deeper simultaneously by scour from tidal run-off and a building of the banks (levees) by the enhanced trapping of sediment by the plants; even in these lower reaches the levees border creeks up to 1m deep. They are populated, however, not by *Puccinellia* but by the woody shrub *Halimione portulacoides* (the sea purslane) (Plate 3). *Halimione* is the only shrub found on British salt-marshes in significant amounts and, in common with other woody species, is not particularly suited to prolonged soil wetness. The presence of two adjacent communities at the same altitudinal level shows that factors other than altitude have a role to play; in this case a drainage difference is probably the critical factor.

Beyond the *Puccinellia/Aster* zone further elevation of the marsh is more gradual with the *Puccinellia* persisting and forming quite a broad expanse of turf from which the *Aster* eventually all but disappears. Subsequently, however, the *Puccinellia* gives way to *Halimione* spreading from the creek levees and at the same time the creek levees begin to be invaded by *Elymus pycnanthus* (sea couch). This is a bluish grass superficially resembling a very much enlarged variant of the common couch grass which is such a notorious garden pest.

Behind the *Elymus* belt lies a broad band of rather dwarf mixed marsh. The mixed marsh or general salt-marsh (GSM) community as it is commonly called, is abundant on the east coast but is usually restricted elsewhere; on the south coast it has been ousted by the ubiquitous *Spartina*. Floristically it is by far the richest community on marshes and contains the particularly attractive species *Armeria maritima* (thrift/sea pink), *Limonium vulgare* (sea

49

lavender) (Plate 3), *Spergularia media* (greater sea-spurrey), and *Cochlearia officinalis* (scurvy-grass), together with the sea plantain (*Plantago maritima*) and sea arrow grass (*Triglochin maritima*). Its position at Welwick is somewhat anomalous and might be the result of past human interference; normally it occurs much lower in the marsh, immediately behind the lower *Puccinellia*. However, the creek system does not extend into this zone and, while slightly higher tides are necessary to flood the soils, they remain wetter for longer periods than the *Elymus*.

To the east of the dwarfed GSM is a taller form of mixed marsh which does intergrade with *Puccinellia* and to the rear more *Elymus, Phragmites australis* (common reed) or *Scirpus maritimus* (sea club rush). The latter two species are generally considered indicative of less saline conditions. In both mixed marsh communities *Festuca rubra* (creeping fescue) appears to be invading to form raised islands and in places these islands have coalesced. In Arctic regions high precipitation and low evapotranspiration result in a large freshwater input and non-saline species can even be found in the middle reaches of the marsh.

A putative scheme of community successions at Welwick is given in Figure 4.1.

3. Factors affecting the succession

Succession results from a complexity of interactions between the plants and their environment and between the plants themselves, and it is not possible within the few pages allotted to comment in any detail on the factors involved. Those who wish for more information are recommended to read the excellent and very readable little monograph on salt-marsh ecology prepared by Long & Mason (1983); another useful text is that of Chapman (1976).

For all the species it is necessary to have some tolerance of salinity, submergence and waterlogging, while in the pioneer zone the lower limits of colonisation may be set by the mechanical removal of seedlings. For *Salicornia*, 2-3 days of continuous exposure are required to allow sufficient root development for anchorage whereas for sea aster it may be 5 days before they are properly anchored. In general terms, however, salinity is overriding in so far as it excludes many plants which could withstand

50

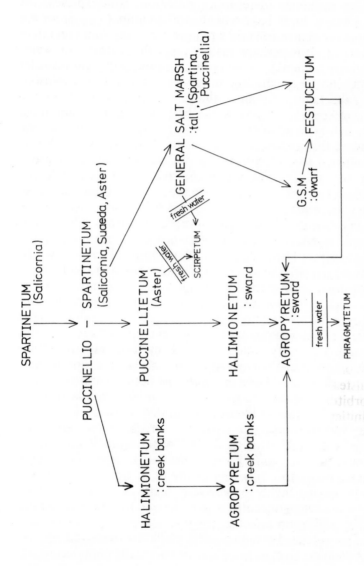

Figure 4.1 Putative scheme of plant succession at Welwick salt-marsh.

both the submergence and the soil waterlogging.

Salinity can interfere with water uptake, can directly be toxic or can exert an influence in terms of nutrition: some species, for example, have a high requirement for sodium (e.g. *Spartina*) although the concentrations they require are many times less than in the sea-water. It is perhaps mainly through its effects on water uptake and the tendency for salts to cause physiological disorder that salinity has a mediating influence on plant distribution. Dissolved salts reduce a plant's ability to extract water from the soil. They effectively impose a 'suction' which the plant must counteract if it is to acquire water. The 'suction' imposed by the coastal waters themselves can amount to -2MPa (20 bars), but if salts are allowed to concentrate, as can happen during long dry periods of inter-tidal exposure in higher reaches of the marsh, the suction effects can become very much greater. To counteract these effects the plant must increase its own 'suction' potentials and one way of achieving this is to absorb and concentrate salts within itself. High internal salinities are, however, normally very injurious to protoplasm and it is these harmful effects which exclude most terrestrial plants from salt-marshes. Most salt-marsh plants can tolerate higher than normal levels of salts in their proto-plasm; they can also concentrate the salts in the cell vacuoles and thereby reduce the levels in the cytoplasm itself. To varying extents species excrete salts and again to varying extents exclude salts and maintain the necessary water-suctions by accumulating high concentrations of non-toxic organic materials such as proline and betaines instead of salt. *Plantago maritima* accumulates the sugar alcohol sorbitol. The need to excrete salt can be particularly acute if soil salinities become suddenly very diluted by rain water or by freshwater inflows into an estuary, for, if the plant had accumulated salts sufficient to extract water from highly saline soil, a diminution of salinity might lead to uncontrolled water uptake and literally to a bursting of the cells. Some plants over-come this by having highly expansive cells or cells of greater than normal volume: high concentrations of ions in the shoots are thus prevented by a dilution effect — the plants appear fleshy and are said to be succulent. In some species salts are removed by the shedding of leaves. Exclusion of salts involves the endodermis, in the young parts of roots a protoplasmic barrier surrounding the centrally-placed water and sugar-conducting tissues and in which there may be an outwardly directed pumping of sodium ions. The endodermis may also be double and in older parts of the root may become very much thickened, forming a physical barrier to salt and water uptake. Salts may also be excluded by the lowering of water intake by a reduction in water loss: the rolling of leaves to reduce the area of exposed surfaces (e.g. *Puccinellia*) or the sinking of stomata (pores in the leaf surface through which water is lost) in furrows, or by particularly high water-use efficiency. The latter is a characteristic of *Spartina* and *Salicornia* and other species where a physiology resembling that in desert plants pertains.

In addition to salinity, soil and plant aeration and the consequences of soil and plant anoxia may also exert a major influence on the zonation of salt-marsh vegetation. Soil waterlogging and the partial or total submergence of vegetation can drastically affect gas-exchange in plant and soil: the soils not only become anoxic but their chemistry is altered also and is to varying degrees potentially damaging to plants.

The first-ever study of salt-marsh aeration to identify and quantify differences between the vegetated zones and temporal changes within zones has been conducted from Hull University's Department of Plant Biology and Genetics in recent years and relates to the marshes at Welwick and Skeffling (Armstrong *et al.* 1985). In this study relationships were sought between species distribution, species characteristics (such as internal gas-space), soil aeration and tidal activity in the various zones of the marsh. Redox potential — the electrical potential of the sediments measured in millivolts and indicative of, among other things, the presence of oxygen and phytoxins such as ferrous (FeII) iron and hydrogen sulphide — was used as an index of aeration. Figure 4.2 shows how aeration patterns can vary with tidal activity, position and hence zonation; 400-600mV indicates extremely well-aerated conditions; -100mV represents intensely anaerobic (reducing) conditions.

It came as no surprise to find the *Spartina* soils so poorly aerated: this species together with other plants of the low marsh is permeated by a very well-developed system of gas-spaces and, at least when not submerged, the roots can obtain large quantities of oxygen from the aerial parts and the atmosphere by diffusion in these gas-spaces (aerenchyma). Furthermore, oxygen can diffuse

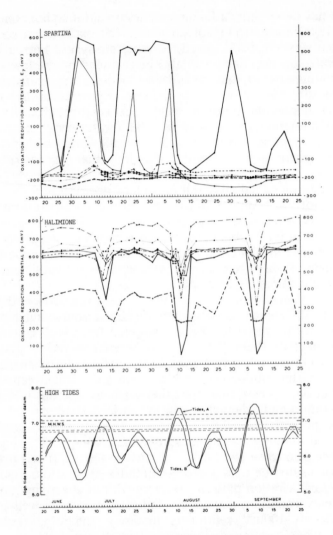

Figure 4.2 Contrasting patterns of soil aeration between two of the lower salt-marsh communities at Welwick salt-marsh — *Spartina* flats and creek-bank *Halimione*. Data obtained as oxidation-reduction potentials at permanently installed electrodes. The patterns are chiefly a function of frequency and duration of tidal flooding. Key to sampling depths (cm):-

●————● 1.5 cm	●—·—·● 10.0 cm
●————● 2.5 cm	●·········● 20.0 cm
●— — —● 5.0 cm	●— — —● 30.0 cm
●—··—··● 7.0 cm	

from root to soil bringing about an amelioration in the conditions in the immediate vicinity of the roots. The plants cannot remain properly aerated when fully submerged however, particularly in darkness, and it is likely that types of anaerobic metabolism will ensure survival over these periods. Colonisers such as *Spartina* are also helped by an ability to germinate in the anoxic muds. (Rice is another wetland species in which this occurs.)

For *Halimione* and *Elymus* also, the aeration factor probably plays a very important role in determining their position on the marsh. In these plants a poorer development of internal gas space correlates with a preference for better aerated habitats.

4. Regression

Salt-marshes do not spread indefinitely. Where tidal conditions change, so that erosion exceeds deposition, a micro-cliff may form eroding the mature marsh surface as it retreats landward. Such a cliff is to be found at Skeffling at the margin of the *Puccinellia* zone although here there is a healthy sward of *Spartina* stretching out for at least 50m in front of it.

Regression may also occur because of the die-back of *Spartina*: it is thought that decaying accumulated organic matter from dense stands of the plant can in certain circumstances cause toxic extremes of soil anaerobiosis. This weakens the plants and the sward begins to erode. This is happening in places on the north bank of the Humber at the present time but seems to be associated with an influx of very mobile sediment which builds up around the *Spartina*. This causes permanent pools to form and the *Spartina* to be partially submerged always. This situation will reduce the effectiveness of the internal aeration in the plant and reduce vigour.

5. Primary production, nutrient balance and energy flow

Currently, there is a tremendous upsurge of interest world-wide in nutrient cycling, nutrient balances, primary production, decomposition, and energy-flow in the salt-marsh ecosystem. Because of the complex nature of such topics there is not room to discuss them here. For an introduction to such topics the reader is recommended to consult Long & Mason (1983).

Wetlands as a whole are highly productive, accounting for 2.3% of the world's net productivity yet occupying only 0.4% of the world's surface. Only the tropical rain forests equal the net productivity of salt-marshes. The productivity of the salt-marsh is aided in no small measure by the activities of the *Spartinas* which belong to that physiologically and economically important group known as the C-4 plants. This group, which also includes maize, effects much higher rates of assimilation than normal: their photo-synthetic mechanism is more efficient than in the C-3 group (to which most plants belong). Much of this production will support animals either on the marsh or on the mudflats and elsewhere when it is exported as detritus. Even on salt-marshes, however, plant productivity may be sub-optimal, limited by nitrogen and phosphorus availability due to the chemical processes taking place under anoxic conditions.

6. Conservation

Salt-marshes world-wide are under threat, from reclamation for both agricultural and industrial purposes, from pollution, and even from the leisure industry. In Britain the scale of the problem is very worrying. Long & Mason (1983) report that over the past thirty years, 15% of the salt-marsh in England and Wales has been lost and that there is a potential threat to a further 20%. About 4000ha of salt-marsh in Britain classified as Sites of Special Scientific Interest (SSSI) have been reclaimed since 1950.

The justification for such destruction for agricultural purposes now seems very hard to understand, viewed in the light of the gross over-production of cereals in Europe and the consequent cost to the taxpayer; in addition, government monies are often spent in subsidising the reclamation work itself.

Industrial pressures on inter-tidal areas have been considerable and proposals still continue for the siting there of oil-refineries, chemical plants, airports, tidal barriers, or simply dumps for industrial waste. Even leisure activities such as the creation of marinas have been eating into remaining sites. Teesside has been quoted as an extreme example of salt-marsh removal having lost all but 6% of the 2400ha of marsh present in the early nineteenth century. In the Thames region oil refineries and even much of London itself are situated on former marsh. With the spread of industrialisation comes the ever-increasing threat of pollution and on the Humber we have been made critically aware of the dangers in recent years.

From all this we can hardly but conclude that there is an urgent need for conservation and in this context it should perhaps be noted that the retention of salt-marshes can make a significant and low-cost contribution to sea and estuary defences. For the Humber we can only hope that serious pollution and further destruction can be avoided and do everything within our power to retain the fine examples of the salt-marsh environment that still survive.

References

Armstrong, W., Wright, E.J., Lythe, S. & Gaynard, T.J. 1985. Plant zonation and the effects of the spring-neap tidal cycle on soil aeration in a Humber Salt Marsh. *Journal of Ecology* 73, 323-39.

Chapman, V.J. 1976. *Coastal Vegetation* 2nd edn. Pergamon Press.

Long, S.P. & Mason, C.F. 1983. *Saltmarsh Ecology* 1st edn. Blackie.

IV

Life in the Humber

(B) Invertebrate animals

N.V. Jones

Introduction

1. The distribution of invertebrates within the Humber

2. The productivity of invertebrates in the Humber

Introduction

Living in estuaries is difficult because the chemistry of the water changes with the tides, freshwater flow, time of year etc. The main variable is salinity which causes osmotic problems for organisms. By this we mean that the water and chemical composition of the bodies of animals have to be fairly stable and that maintaining this stability is difficult if the composition of the outside medium is variable. In freshwater, the tendency for water to enter the animal has to be countered by an increase in loss of water. In sea-water on the other hand, the animal tends to lose water and consequently it has to increase its intake. Different species have different capacities for the regulation necessary in either of these extremes and even more so in estuarine situations where the salinity can change very rapidly. This means that the distribution of animals within an estuary will be determined by their capacity to control body fluids (osmoregulation). Animals that are adapted to narrow ranges of salinity (either low as in freshwater, or high as in sea-water) are termed stenohaline, whereas those that can stand wide variations are called euryhaline animals.

The second main feature of estuaries is their turbidity which has been described elsewhere in this volume. This means that the habitats available to estuarine organisms are predominantly sedimentary, that is mud or sand. Such physical characters of the environment obviously affect the kinds of animals that will occur there. Mud and sand will be colonised by burrowers, feeding mainly on the organic material in or on the sediment or by filterers using the material suspended in the water. These animals may then form the diet of carnivores found in the sediment, above it (such as fish and shrimps) or when it is exposed (e.g. birds). Estuarine areas are very rich in organic material washed down by rivers or brought in from the sea. They, therefore, provide a good place to settle as long as the organisms can put up with the chemical conditions and like mud! Indeed, estuaries are among the most productive natural environments on earth.

These general considerations lead us to an examination of the Humber fauna under two headings (1) the distribution of animals within the estuary and (2) the performance (or productivity) of these animals in the areas in which they occur.

1. The distribution of invertebrates within the Humber

The change in salinity along the length of any estuary is reflected in the communities of animals that occur there. This is true of the Humber as is illustrated in Figure 4.3. This illustration is based on data presented by Rees *et al.* (1982) and includes the number of species (or taxonomic groups) recorded in studies of the inter-tidal areas of both banks as well as those collected from a boat. While the studies are not strictly comparable because of differences in techniques, each does produce the same general pattern. The upper (freshwater) end of the estuary is home for a relatively sparse fauna with the number of species generally increasing towards the seaward end where the most diverse fauna is found. Some sites, however, show a decrease in diversity which may be due to local pollution or to the lack of variation in physical conditions.

The fauna of the estuary shows zonation of the species within the general pattern illustrated above. Some of them will be

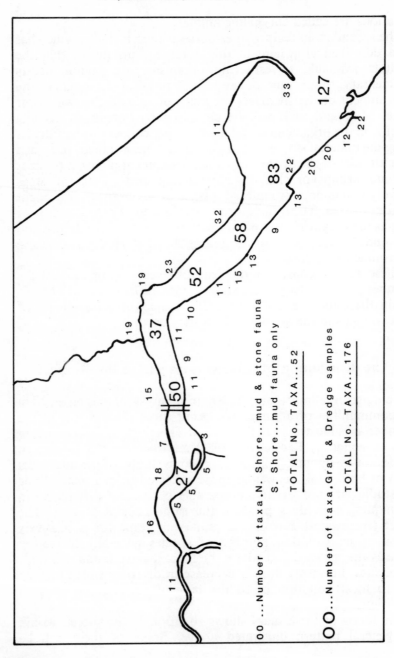

Figure 4.3 Distribution of invertebrate animals in the Humber. (Based on Rees *et al.*, 1982)

generalists (euryhaline) which will occur over a range of salinities, and, therefore, over a length of the estuary. Others will be specialists (oligohaline) that can only live at low salinities (upper end of the estuary) or at high salinities (the marine end). There will be a transition zone in the middle where an overlap of these faunal elements may occur. This is illustrated by examination of Table 4.1 which is reproduced from Rees *et al.* (1982). Note that the oligochaete worms are generally found in the upper to middle estuary with *Tubificoides benedeni* being found only in the latter region. The polychaete worms on the other hand are found mostly in the outer and middle estuary except for *Nereis diversicolor* (Plate 4) and *Manayunkia aestuarina* which are found throughout the estuary. Most of the molluscs occur in the outer and middle regions.

The Crustacea collected in the inter-tidal area (Table 4.1) show a marine distribution except for *Corophium volutator* but these animals are found more commonly in the water body. Figure 4.4 shows the distribution of one group of Crustacea (the mysids) as recorded by the Humber Estuary Committee (Rees *et al.* 1982). The shrimp, *Neomysis integer*, occurs in the upper to middle region, whereas the other species are mainly outer estuary animals.

It is clear from the above that there is a shift in importance of the various groups as we move along the estuary. This is not only seen in the number of species of each group of animals, but also in the numbers of individuals found. This is shown in Figure 4.5 which shows that the upper estuary produced large numbers of Crustacea but that the middle and outer estuary were dominated by polychaete worms.

This kind of information derived from surveys of different parts of the estuary illustrates the zonation of animals, reflecting the varying conditions that prevail along the estuary. More detailed work shows that the zonation referred to varies with season and that the dominance of a species may not be repeated to the same degree each year. Within each zone there will be shown another gradient of conditions and, consequently, of animal distribution. This will occur at right angles to the shore and be determined by the tidal range. An example of this inter-tidal zonation is given below and is illustrated in Figure 4.6.

SITE	UPPER ESTUARY														LOWER ESTUARY				
	1	1A	2	2A	3	3A	4	4A	5	5A	6	6A	7	7A	8	8A	9	9A	10
ANNELIDA																			
OLIGOCHAETA																			
Enchytraeidae	•	•	•	•	•	•	•	•	•	•	•	•			•	•	•	•	•
Paranais litoralis	•	•	•	•	•					•	•				•	•			
Tubifex costatus	•	•	•	•	•	•					•	•							
Tubificoides benedeni									•	•	•	•	•	•	•				
Tubificoides pseudogaster																•			
POLYCHAETA																			
Nereis diversicolor	•	•	•	•	•	•	•	•	•	•	•	•			•	•	•		
Nephtys hombergii													•	•	•	•			•
Nephtys cirrosa															•	•	•	•	•
Eteone longa						•	•			•	•	•	•	•	•	•	•	•	•
Anaitides maculata															•	•			
Syllidae																•			
Sphaerodoridae															•				
Pygospio elegans			•		•	•	•	•	•	•	•	•	•		•				
Streblospio shrubsolii	•		•	•	•	•		•	•	•	•	•			•				
Polydora (ciliata)			•	•			•		•			•				•			
Spio filicornis																•		•	•
Spiophanes bombyx															•	•		•	•
Nerine (cirratulus)															•	•		•	•
(Tharyx marioni)															•			•	
Paraonis fulgens															•			•	•
Orbinidae			•				•		•	•					•			•	
Capitella capitata						•	•		•	•	•	•	•	•	•	•	•		
Arenicola marina										•	•								
Ampharetidae																			•
Ophelia rathkei																		•	
Manayunkia aestuarina	•			•	•	•	•	•					•	•					
Lanice conchilega																			•
CRUSTACEA																			
AMPHIPODA																			
Haustorius arenarius																•		•	•
Bathyporeia sp.															•	•		•	
Urothoe sp.																		•	
Corophium volutator	•	•	•			•	•	•	•	•	•	•		•					
Corophium arenarium																•		•	•
TANAIDACEA																			
Tanaissus lilljeborgi																•			
CUMACEA																			
ISOPODA																			•
Cyathura carinata					•														
Eurydice pulchra																	•	•	
MOLLUSCA																			
BIVALVIA																			
Macoma balthica	•	•	•	•	•	•						•		•	•	•	•	•	•
(Modiolus)																•	•	•	•
Cerastoderma edule															•	•	•	•	•
GASTROPODA																			
Hydrobia ulvae					•										•	•	•	•	•
NEMERTINI																			

**Table 4.1   The Inter-tidal fauna of the south shore of the Humber.
(Based on Rees *et al.*, 1982)**

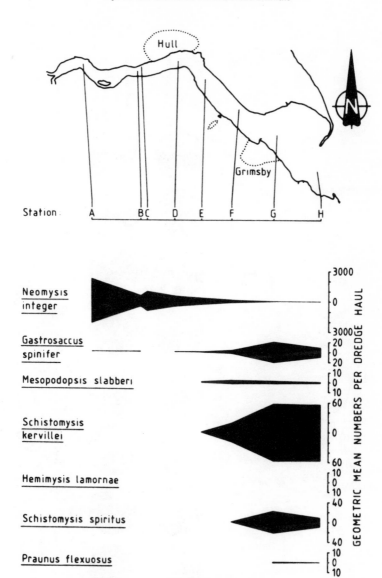

Figure 4.4 Distribution and relative abundance of mysid shrimps in the Humber. (From Rees *et al.*, 1982).

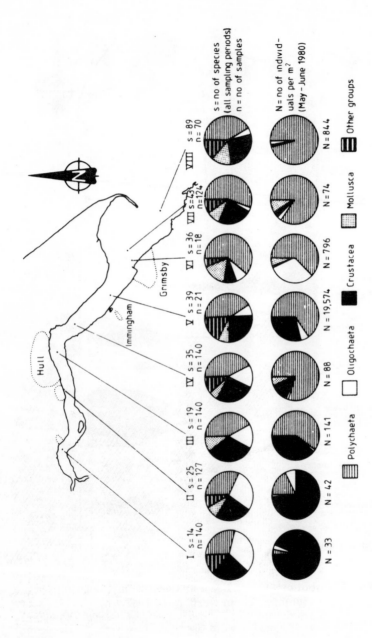

Figure 4.5   Pie diagram showing the composition of faunal assemblages at sites on the bed of the Humber. (From Rees *et al.*, 1982).

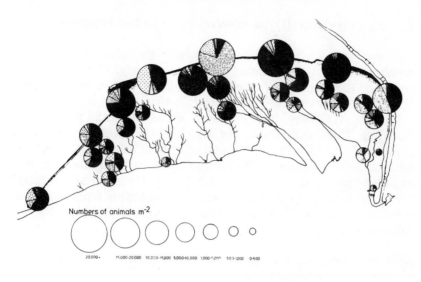

Numbers of animals m⁻²

20.000+   15,000-20,000 10,000-15,000 5,000-10,000 1,000-5,000 500-1000 0-500

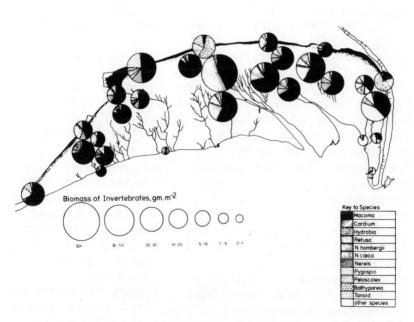

Biomass of Invertebrates, gm. m⁻²

5>   30-50   20-30   10-20   5-10   1-5   0-1

Key to Species
Macoma
Cardium
Hydrobia
Retusa
N hombergii
N caeca
Nereis
Pygospio
Peloscolex
Bathyporeia
Tanaid
other species

Figure 4.6   The distribution of numbers of animals and their biomass at different shore levels at sites in Spurn Bight. (Key, 1983).

2. The productivity of invertebrates in the Humber

The previous section considered where the various species of invertebrate animals occurred within the estuary. This section will consider the density of these populations and how well they perform in terms of biological productivity.

Ratcliffe (1979) studied the fauna of the inter-tidal mudflats at Skeffling, Paull and Hessle. He described the communities found at these sites, which fall within quite different salinity regimes, and estimated their numbers, the biomass (weight of animals per m²) and their productivity (the amount of animal material produced per m² in a year). Table 4.2 is selected information from his thesis covering Paull and Skeffling and is presented here to illustrate the following points:

(a) The community at the two sites is composed of different species (see Section 1 above).

(b) In relation to Skeffling, Paull had: higher numbers of animals per square metre, lower biomass, higher productivity.

(c) These figures reflect the size of the various species and the speed at which they grow and reproduce.

The mudflats at Paull are considerably smaller than those at Skeffling but it is clear that they are very productive. The figures given in Table 4.2 are estimates based on means taken from various sites within the area. This does not reflect the contribution of various parts of the beach which, of course, may not be homogeneous. Key (1983) studied the Spurn Bight area in detail and Figure 4.6 shows his summary of numbers and biomass recorded at different levels on the shore at various sites within the Bight. It is clear that, in general, the highest numbers of invertebrates occur high on the beach whereas the highest biomass is found lower down the shore. This is a reflection of the distribution of the larger (and, therefore, heavier) animals which tend to occur more commonly lower on the shore than the smaller species and individuals. On the basis of his study, Key divided the shore into four areas: a strip of *Spartina*, a band of upper shore silt (TOPSILT), an extensive area of midshore mud (MIDMUD) and a lower shore sandy area (SAND). Table 4.3 shows his figures for biomass and productivity for each of the areas. These show that

SPECIES	PAULL			SKEFFLING		
	Mean Annual Density (nos.m⁻²)	Mean Annual Biomass (gm⁻²)	Production (gm⁻² y⁻¹)	Mean Annual Density (nos. m⁻²)	Mean Annual Biomass (gm⁻²)	Production (gm⁻² y⁻¹)
Eteone longa				500	0.25	0.5
Nephtys hombergi	8,000	9.3	15.0	500	3.25	6.2
Nereis diversicolor				500	0.58	0.9
Peloscolex benedini				1,000	0.24	0.7
Pygospio elegans				5,000	0.45	1.4
Streblospio shrubsoli						
Macoma balthica	30,000	0.05	0.3	500	0.045	0.1
Retusa obtusa	40,000	0.04	0.2	12,000	15.0	12.0
Harpacticoidea				1,000	0.40	0.8
Nematoda	200,000	6.0	18.0	25,000	0.045	0.2
Lumbricillus lineatus				100,000	0.10	0.5
Manayunkia aestuarina	15,000	0.45	1.4			
Corophium volutator	4,000	0.2	0.6			
TOTALS	297,000	16.0	35.5	146,000	20.4	23.3

Community P:B ratio.　　　　　Paull = 2.21:1　　　　　Skeffling = 1.1:1

Table 4.2 A summary of data on the invertebrate communities of Paull and Skeffling mudflats. (Based on Ratcliffe, 1979).

	BIOMASS	PRODUCTION (Annual)

SPARTINA ZONE (91 ha)

	BIOMASS	PRODUCTION (Annual)
Hydrobia ulvae (Pennant)	14.1 t	14.1 t*
Hediste diversicolor (Müller)	8.7 t	22.2 t
Edukemius benedii (d'Udekem)	1.3 t	-
Total	24.4 t (268 Kg ha^{-1})	36.4 t (400 Kg ha^{-1})

UPPER SHORE SILT (332 ha)

	BIOMASS	PRODUCTION (Annual)
Macoma balthica (L.)	59.6 t	123.9 t
Hydrobia ulvae	13.1 t	13.1 t*
Hediste diversicolor	12.7 t	42.0 t
Total	91.5 t (276 Kg ha^{-1})	182.3 t (549 Kg ha^{-1})

MIDSHORE MUD (1747 ha)

	BIOMASS	PRODUCTION (Annual)
Macoma balthica	321.0 t	229.0 t
Cerastoderma edule (L.)	134.0 t	80.5 t
Nephtys spp.	64.5 t	147.0 t
Hediste diversicolor	25.3 t	83.4 t
Hydrobia ulvae	19.0 t	19.0 t*
Retusa obtusa (Montagu)	5.1 t	24.0 t
Total	571.3 t (327 Kg ha^{-1})	582.9 t (334 Kg ha^{-1})

DOWNSHORE SAND (786 ha)

	BIOMASS	PRODUCTION (Annual)
Macoma balthica	32.0 t	8.3 t
Nephtys spp.	9.3 t	21.3 t
Cerastoderma edule	3.9 t	2.4 t
Total	46.9 t (59.7 Kg ha^{-1})	32.2 t (41 Kg ha^{-1})

	BIOMASS	PRODUCTION (Annual)
TOTAL FOR WHOLE AREA	734.1 t (248 Kg ha^{-1})	833.8 t (282 Kg ha^{-1})

*Productivity figures were not available for *Hydrobia*. this estimate assumes a P:B ratio of 1 and is, therefore, likely to be a considerable underestimate. All these figures are liable to various degrees of under or over-estimation and exclude *Mya* and mysids etc. In general, the uppershore sites are likely to be underestimated whereas the lower shore figures are more likely to be overestimates.

Table 4.3 Estimated biomass and production of four communities on the Spurn Bight mudflats. (Key, 1983). Figures are given only for the main species.

Estuary	*Hydrobia ulvae*	*Macoma balthica*	*Bathyporeia pilosa*	*Haustorius arenarius*	*Cyathura carinata*	*Corophium volutator*	*Corophium arenarium*	*Arenicola marina*	*Nephtys hombergii*	*Nephtys cirrosa*	*Nereis diversicolor*
Humber	24,000	5,300	1,600	150	60	65,000	39,500	—	700	800	7,700
Severn	18,100	884	14,400	40	40	2,400	1,600	49	432	20	6,800
Tamar (Devon)	28,420	76	A	A	378	11,000	A	3	500	A	3,030
Exe (Devon)	13,280	32	2,180	8	A	—	312	136	24	8	132
Towy (Wales)	57,056	2,400	8,576	A	496	17,136	2,464	—	—	A	1,212
Dovey (Wales)	45,900	7,227	704	A	A	63,000	4,411	11	—	A	97
Thames	11,500	1,600	A	common	common	2,000	1,700	68	common	—	250
Dee (Cheshire)	12,500	2,000	—	8	A	24,800	10,000	16	—	A	416
Ythan (Scotland)	80,000	common	frequent	—	A	60,000	—	common	A	A	340

— = Maximum density unknown
A = Not recorded

Table 4.4 Maximum densities (per m²) of shore-dwelling species present in the Humber compared with those recorded in other British estuaries. (Rees et al., 1982)

the TOPSILT area has a large number of small animals that are more productive than the larger animals further down the shore. The sandy areas are much less productive than the mud.

Table 4.4 (from Rees *et al.* 1982) shows a comparison of maximum densities of invertebrates recorded in British estuaries. It is clear from this table that the Humber holds its own with any of our estuaries and, indeed, has denser populations of most of the species that are also recorded elsewhere. Tables 4.2 and 4.3 show that these populations are also very productive. In fact, they compare favourably with figures produced for estuaries elsewhere.

The Spurn Bight area covers about 3000ha and Key (1983) estimated that the area held about 734 tonnes of invertebrates at any one time and that these produced about 834 tonnes of organic material in a year. This latter figure is generally what would be available to predators such as birds, fish and shrimps. The area holds important populations of birds (see Goodall, 4.D) but Key estimated that they may only remove about 2-3% of this production. The remainder must be taken by fish and shrimps on the flats or be exported to deeper water where it forms the diet of other species. The productivity of these mudflats may, therefore, be important for species living outside the area and for commercial as well as other species.

The Humber may be muddy and dirty looking but it is clearly very much alive, and very productive. If you like mud, and many animals do, it is a great place to be!

References

Key, R.S. 1983. Ecology of the infauna of Spurn Bight mudflats: an area proposed for reclamation. Unpublished Ph.D. Thesis: University of Hull.

Ratcliffe, P.J. 1979. An ecological study of the inter-tidal invertebrates of the Humber Estuary. Unpublished Ph.D. Thesis: University of Hull.

Rees, H.L., Barnett, B.E. and Urquhart, C. Biological Surveillance *in* Gameson, A.L.H. Ed. 1982 *The Quality of the Humber Estuary, 1961-81*. Published by the Yorkshire Water Authority on behalf of the Humber Estuary Committee.

IV

Life in the Humber

(C)   Fishes

D.B. Lewis

Introduction

1.   Factors affecting the distribution of fish within the estuary

2.   Reproduction

3.   Feeding

Introduction

A visitor to the Humber, looking from the bridge or its banks, could be forgiven for assuming that the fish life contained within those swirling turbid waters, is most probably very meagre or non-existent. In fact, there is a large and diverse fish fauna. Rees (1981), lists some sixty species which have been recorded from within the confines of the estuary; a list which is almost certainly not definitive. What we are going to consider is: the kinds of fish which occur in the Humber; what parts of it they inhabit and how they survive, feed, and reproduce in an environment of changing salinity, turbidity, and tidal scour.

As in the case of invertebrates, species distribution is not uniform throughout the estuary. Fishes may be thought of as belonging to one of the following groups:

(a)   Marine species which enter the mouth of the estuary, where the salinity is much the same as that of the sea; e.g. tope

(Galeorhinus galeus), spurdog *(Squalus acanthias)*, herring *(Clupea harengus)*, mackerel *(Scomber scrombrus)*, turbot *(Scophthalmus maximus)*, saithe *(Pollachius virens)*.

(b) Estuarine species, which live in the main body of the estuary, and can tolerate low and variable salinities for prolonged periods; e.g. flounder *(Platichthys flesus)*, common goby *(Pomatoschistus microps)*, greater pipefish *(Syngnathus acus)*.

(c) Fish which normally inhabit fresh water, but for one reason or another sometimes occur at the top of the estuary, where salinity is very low; e.g. tench *(Tinca tinca)*, carp *(Cyprinius carpio)*, silver bream *(Blicca bjoerkna)*, bleak *(Alburnus alburnus)*, roach *(Rutilus rutilus)*, pike *(Esox lucius)*.

(d) Fish which use the estuary as a highway, while en route from the sea to fresh water to breed (anadromous), or vice versa (catachromous). Anadromous forms include the salmon *(Salmo salar)*, the sea trout *(Salmo trutta)*, and formerly the sturgeon *(Acipenser sturio)*. Catadromous forms include the eel *(Anguilla anguilla)*.

Within the above groups there are fish which may occur: on the bottom, e.g. plaice *(Pleuronectes platessa)*, sole *(Solea solea)*, and thornback ray *(Raja clavata)*; in mid-water, e.g. cod *(Gadus morhua)* and whiting *(Merlangius merlangus)*; in the surface waters, e.g. herring and mackerel.

1. Factors affecting the distribution of fish within the estuary

Salinity is the main factor which determines the distribution of fish within the estuary. Tidal scour, temperature variations, and turbidity are also important factors.

Some fishes are only able to live in water, the salinity of which is almost constant (termed stenohaline). One such fish is the marine hagfish *(Myxine glutinosa)* which is restricted to the sea and never enters the estuary. Fish such as the cod, haddock, thornbacked ray, sole and plaice can withstand a lowering of salinity, to varying degrees. They are thus able to enter the estuary, but tend to occur at the lower end. Several species of freshwater fish are caught by anglers and eel fishermen in the upper Humber. These include the tench and others cited above. How long the majority of these can survive in brackish-water is not known. The pike is one exception which occurs commonly in the brackish-waters of the Baltic. So too is the stickleback (*Gasterosteus aculeatus*), which is common in brackish-water.

The flounder and common goby are estuarine fish *par excellence*. These animals flourish in a wide range of salinities and are termed euryhaline. The common goby (*P.microps*) can be found in small pools in the mud, high up on the beach at Paull. These pools may be filled with water of relatively high salinity at high tide whereas during the low tide period the water in the pools may be diluted with rainwater, or have its salinity raised by evaporation on hot summer days. The sand goby (*P.minutus*) also occurs in the estuary; however, it is not so euryhaline as its relative, and thus lives in the more saline water of the lower estuary.

Survival in the sea, estuary, and freshwater depends upon the ability of the fish to control the salt concentration in its blood and tissues: i.e. their ability to osmoregulate.

In sea-water there is a tendency for animals to lose water whereas in freshwater the converse is true. This is due to the relative concentration of salts within and outside the animals and the resulting phenomenon of osmosis.

Figures 4.7 a and b indicate how both marine and fresh water fishes osmoregulate.

A marine fish (Fig. 4.7a) loses water from the gills, skin and in the urine. In order to replace this, the fish drinks sea-water and produces small quantities of urine. However, the sea-water imbibed contains a large number of substances, in addition to sodium chloride (common salt), in solution. If the intake of these substances continued unchecked, they would accumulate, until their concentrations were the same as that of the surrounding sea-water. This would impair the functioning of the fish. The fish deals with these surplus substances by concentrating the sulphate, magnesium, and calcium ions in the intestine and eliminating them in the faeces while sodium and potassium ions are eliminated into the sea by special secretory cells located in the gills, the lining of the buccal cavity (mouth), and the oesophagus (throat).

A freshwater fish (Fig. 4.7b) absorbs water through the skin and gills; in response it produces large quantities of dilute urine. Some

73

(a) MARINE TELEOST

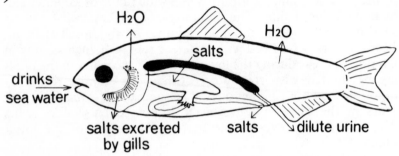

(b) FRESH WATER TELEOST

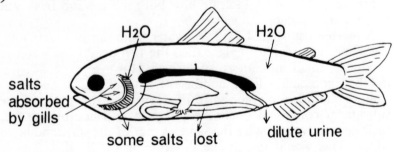

Figure 4.7   A representation of the water balance mechanisms of fish in (a) marine and (b) freshwater environments.

salts are lost by diffusion from the gills, and in the faeces and urine. These salts are replaced from the food, and by absorption via special cells in the gills.

Fish that live in changing salinity conditions will clearly need to have suitable adjusting mechanisms. Some examples of osmoregularity ability of fishes are the following: when salmon enter freshwater from the sea, there is a dramatic increase in the production of urine.

Urine produced in the sea   10- 15 ml/kg/day
Urine produced in freshwater   200-400 ml/kg/day

The fish maintains its blood concentration in the sea at 340 m-osmoles/1, and this only drops to 328 in freshwater.

In comparison, the eel's blood in sea-water has a concentration of 428 m-osmoles/1, and 346 in freshwater — the thick covering of mucus secreted by the fish helps to reduce water movements through the skin. The flounder is characteristically found in brackish-water but is not so good an osmoregulator as the salmon and eel; in sea-water the blood is maintained at 528 m-osmoles/1, whereas in brackish-water the level maintained is 286 m-osmoles/1. Despite this, young flounders are able to live in freshwater for years. North Sea herring can withstand salinities in a range 6-40‰ chloride (181-1212 m-osmoles/1). This enables it to move into, and range widely in, the Baltic.

Osmoregulatory ability is then a pre-requisite for life in an estuary and it determines the distribution of species within the estuary. The other factors which affect the distribution of fishes within the estuary, namely tidal scour, temperature, and turbidity generally affect breeding and/or feeding as well as exerting direct physical effects on the fish.

2. Reproduction

The conditions obtaining in the Humber and other estuaries, pose many problems for spawning fish. Floods cause rapid falls in salinity, which eggs and larvae may be unable to tolerate. The increased volume of water may result in eggs and larvae being flushed from the estuary. Drought, and consequent low river run-off, frequently results in lower oxygen levels as well as increasing tidal scour, which leads to sediment being returned to the upper reaches of the estuary. The deposition of silt on demersal eggs (i.e. those laid on the bottom) can result in high mortality, due in part to a reduction in oxygen. Bacteria, fungi and protozoa flourish on silt-covered demersal eggs, constituting a common cause of mortality. High levels of suspended matter in water are often associated with low oxygen levels, which adversely affect egg and larval development. Temperatures can oscillate rapidly in estuaries and some authorities report occasions when abrupt decreases in temperature have caused large mortalities among larval and juvenile estuarine fish.

Plaice, dabs, sole and many other species of fish, including the flounder, migrate out to sea to spawn, where conditions are relatively uniform. In this way they presumably escape the vagaries of estuarine conditions. Studies on estuarine fish in South Africa showed that the dominant species had an extended spawning season of up to eight months. In this way short periods of adverse conditions would affect only a small proportion of the total eggs and larvae produced.

The fish which breed successfully in the Humber have adopted tactics which include nest building, brooding and viviparity (live hearing), which enable them to contend with the vagaries of the estuarine 'climate'.

Estuaries are generally considered to be some of the most productive regions on earth and it is because of the readily available food supplies that, despite the variable conditions, so many species of marine fish use these regions as nursery grounds. Riley (1979) found twenty-four species of juvenile fish in autumn fine-net trawls in the Humber.

We can now turn to consider the reproductive habits of some Humber fishes, which illustrate the various strategies adopted in response to the estuarine environment.

Salmon (and Sea Trout)
Although the numbers of salmon caught in the Humber and Yorkshire rivers have declined over recent years, some fish still do make their way through the estuary to spawn in rivers such as the Ouse and Ure (Parry, 1983; Rees, 1982). The young salmon migrate down-stream as smolts, i.e. two years after spawning, to return to the sea to feed and grow, before returning as adults to spawn. One reason given for the decline is the poor water

76

condition in the upper Humber and river Ouse. In this region, organic pollution results in de-oxygenation of the water; this is particularly so in warm weather and when the flow of water is reduced. Adult salmon migrate up-river only when conditions are favourable, i.e. they wait until there is a high freshwater flow. The smolts, however, perform their down-river migration in spring and early summer, when temperatures are rising and the river flow is falling. Thus when the fish reach the polluted region of the river Ouse and upper Humber, the oxygen levels are frequently too low to sustain them. Latterly the Yorkshire Water Authority has improved the numbers of returning adults, by transporting smolts from the river Ure, to Brough Haven: thus by-passing the region of de-oxygenation.

Smelt
This small relative of the salmon is an inshore fish which enters the estuaries in winter, migrating to spawn up-stream in freshwater in spring. Some individuals may spend all their lives in some estuaries.

The eel
This fish spawns some 2500-3000 miles away in the Sargasso Sea. The eggs hatch and become small transparent leaf-like Leptocephalus larvae, which drift in the Gulf Stream and North Atlantic Drift for 2½-3 years before entering the North Sea. While over the continental shelf the Leptocephalus larvae metamorphose into the transparent eel-shaped 'glass eels'. A second 'metamorphosis' occurs in coastal waters, when the pigment is laid down and the 'glass eels' become elvers, many of which stay at the mouths of rivers or on the sea-shore. However, countless thousands move into the Humber and other estuaries, and finally make their way into freshwater. Tidal currents in estuaries pose a problem for small fish such as elvers but their behavioural responses have become adapted to take advantage of estuarine currents in the following way: on the flood tide the elvers swim up into the water and are carried up the estuary by the current, while on the ebb they bury themselves in the mud and thus avoid being swept back down-stream. Once in freshwater, the eels feed and grow for several years, they are muddy brown above and yellowish golden on the sides, and are known as yellow eels. During their

return journey to the sea to breed, they change colour, when the back becomes almost black and the belly silver; at this stage they are termed silver eels. Other changes occur, notably an increase in the size of the eye, which is an adaptation for life in the ocean's middle depths. The return journey to the Sargasso is shrouded in mystery, and some authorities doubt whether they ever regain the Sargasso. It is suggested that the population is maintained by American eels. Elvers entering the Humber in May will have travelled around the north of Scotland into the North Sea before entering the estuary and then proceed inland into the Trent and Ouse systems.

Plaice
First year plaice (O-group), which occur in the Humber, are probably spawned in late March and early April between Baymans Hole and Flamborough to the south (Riley, 1975). The planktonic eggs drift south and hatch into larvae which continue in the upper layers of the water, feeding on the plankton, until summer when they metamorphose into small flatfish, and some enter the Humber in September. Mortality during the planktonic egg and larval stages is very high, being in the region of 99%. Samples taken in the Humber showed that O-group plaice prefer flat, fine or muddy sand in sandy shallow areas from the mouth of the estuary to a little up-stream of Hull, where the salinity is 17‰ (equivalent to about half strength sea-water). As winter approaches and the temperature falls, these small fish tend to move from the nursery grounds into deeper warmer water. Evidence from other areas has shown that for every hundred small plaice coming into the shallows from the plankton, only two will survive the winter.

Sole
Sole spawn in spring, their eggs occurring in greatest numbers off the Lincolnshire coast although small numbers are taken as far north as Flamborough, and in the Humber estuary itself. As with the plaice, some enter the Humber on metamorphosis. Riley (1975) did not find any O-group fish above Immingham, despite the fact that experimentally, this species can withstand almost freshwater. Its distribution may be controlled by the type of sea bed available, and the severe tidal scour.

Sea Snail (Plate 5)

The young of this species of fish which can deal with the tidal-scour and occurs in the main body of the estuary. The pelvic fins of this fish are modified to form a sucker with which it is able to attach itself to rocks, stones and pieces of seaweed. Presumably the fish attaches itself firmly to a rock etc. while the tide is on the ebb or flood, and moves about during periods of slack water.

Flounder

Although small numbers of eggs are laid within the estuary itself, this fish too has its main spawning grounds off-shore (Riley, 1975). The planktonic eggs and larvae drift in the water prior to metamorphosis and settlement on the bottom when they are about 5cm in length. In much the same way as the eel, flounders move up the estuary by swimming up into the water on the flood tide, and maintaining their position by staying on or in the substratum during the ebb tide. In this way young flounders make their way up into freshwater; in the river Hull as far as Hempholme, the river Derwent as far as Kexby, the Market Weighton Canal, the length of the Barmston Drain, and up into the river Ancholme.

Common Goby (Plate 5)

This species is very common in the Humber and is probably the most widespread and abundant fish in British estuaries. The male chooses an empty bivalve shell (cockle, mussel or clam) and excavates a space under the shell to construct his 'nest'. The male defends it against other males, and eventually drives a passing gravid ('pregnant') female into the 'nest': she lays her eggs on the underside of the shell, where they are subsequently fertilised by the male. Both fish have fused pelvic fins which enable them to attach themselves to the shell during egg-laying and fertilisation. The male guards the eggs, and uses his fins to fan them with oxygenated water. Because the eggs are suspended from the shell, and fanned by the male, silt and its accompanying bacteria and fungi do not settle or develop. The eggs are much more difficult to dislodge by water currents than those of other species which may simply be deposited on the surface of the substratum.

79

The greater pipefish (Plate 5)
The eggs of this species are attached to the underside of the male's body and are protected by two flaps of skin, the inside faces of which are highly vascularised (have a large number of fine blood vessels near the surface). This arrangement helps to provide the eggs with oxygen, and also affords them protection against silt and its accompanying bacteria and fungi as well as predation. The availability of sufficient oxygen for the development of the demersal eggs of estuarine and other fishes is a frequent problem. In consequence, many such eggs are yellow in colour, which denotes the presence of high concentrations of carotenoid pigments. These are somewhat similar in function to the red haemoglobin in our blood, and act as an endogenous supply of oxygen.

Stickleback
The male builds a nest of pieces of vegetation in which the female lays the eggs. After fertilisation, the male guards the nest and uses his broad pectoral fins to fan the eggs with clean water: the lower the oxygen tension of the water, the higher the rate of fanning. The eggs are thus protected from water movements, predators, silting and oxygen depletion.

The eel pout
These fish mate in August-September and the fertilised eggs develop within the female and hatch after 3-4 weeks. Remaining inside the female, they continue to grow, nourished by special ovarian tissues. The young are born in December-February, as fully formed, miniature adults; length about 4cm. Internal development helps circumvent most of the problems such as silting-up, outlined above.

3. Feeding

Large numbers of adult and juvenile marine fish move into the Humber, attracted by the rich food supply it affords. One exception to this is the salmon, which does not feed as it moves through the estuary.

Sprat and herring (mixed shoals of juveniles, known as

whitebait) move into the estuary to feed on small planktonic organisms. They catch each food item individually using sight; it is not a passive filtering process. In the summer and autumn cod enter the estuary in the surface waters to feed voraciously on sprat, herring and sand eels.

Mature cod will eat almost anything: herring, haddock, small cod, sand eels, eels, crabs, lug worms, starfish; even plastic coffee cups have been found in their stomachs. The barbel (beard) which protudes from the lower jaw is well endowed with chemosensory organs, which enable the fish to 'taste/smell' the presence of food in the water. The diagnostic white lateral line which extends the length of the body is an organ which perceives vibrations in the water. It enables the fish to navigate, and aids locating food in the turbid waters of the Humber.

Plaice, flounder and sole live and move over the floor of the estuary, where they feed on small invertebrates. The sole has a vast array of barbels on the underside of the head. The small jaws of the plaice are armed with rather insignificant teeth, which are of little use in breaking open bivalve shells. This function is performed by the pharyngeal (throat) teeth; these flattened, molar-like teeth which are carried on musclar pads, crush *Macoma* and cockle shells.

Turbot and brill, two other Humber flat-fish, have very large mouths, with which to engulf other fish. The pharyngeal teeth possess large numbers of fine, sharp teeth, which help to deal with their slippery food.

Weever fish (*Echiichthys vipera*) (Fig. 4.8) is a somewhat laterally flattened fish, with a strongly oblique mouth, which partially buries itself in the sand, from which position it captures passing prey: shrimps, worms, sand eels and crab larvae.

Mullet (*Crenimugil labrosus*) adults are iliophagus taking mouthfulls of mud, and using the gill rakers and pharyngeal pads to sieve organic debris and small invertebrates from it. They also browse algae from rocks and pier piles.

Mature eels eat a wide range of organisms, including large numbers of small fish. Larger eels are frequently associated with discharges rich in organic matter such as occur on the north bank of the Humber.

Greater pipefish (Plate 5) has a slender snout with a small terminal mouth, with which it 'sucks' in small prey, including tiny

81

Figure 4.8   A weever fish in its feeding position.

shrimps, crabs and other crustaceans, herring, cod, goby and other fish larvae.

From the origin to its mouth, régimes of salinity, temperature, oxygen concentration, silting and scouring vary markedly within the Humber, on a daily basis, as the tides ebb and flow, and also seasonally. We have seen the various ways in which a range of fishes has become adapted anatomically, physiologically, and behaviourally, to survival in this ever-changing environment. Survival enables them to utilise the high productivity of the inter-tidal flats and other sources of food in the estuary. Some species are of commercial importance while others, although not used by man directly, are important in the lives of the commercially exploited species, and may contribute considerably to the communities of the estuary as a whole and to the adjacent coastal areas.

Plate 1   Aerial view of Welwick salt-marsh showing the distinctively-zoned vegetation.

Plate 2   Salt-marsh development at the base of the Spurn peninsula.
   (a)   1962 — scattered islands of *Spartina*.
   (b)   1985 — same location — well-established *Puccinellia* community in the foreground fringed by *Spartina* in the background, still extending into Spurn Bight.

Plate 3   Salt-marsh plants.

(a)   *Salicornia* and *Suaeda* dominate
the foreground; *Spartina*, the
background.

(b)   *Spartina anglica* in flower.

(c)   Sea-lavender (*Limonium vulgare*)
in full-bloom.

(d)   Foreground — Sea purslane
(*Halimione portulacoides*)
Background — Sea lavender.

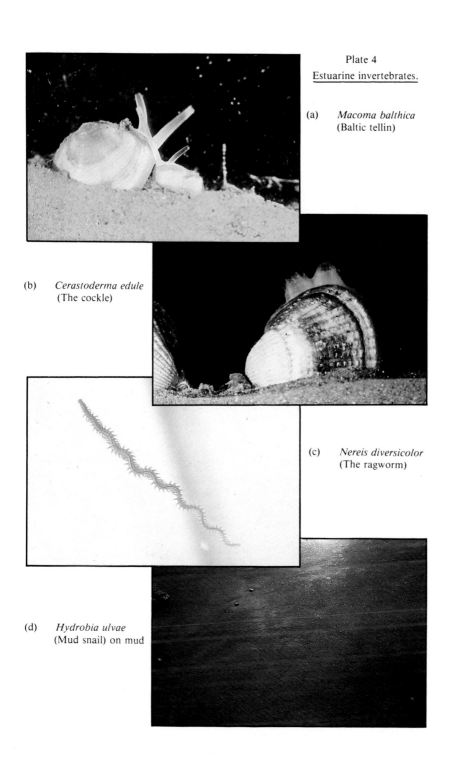

Plate 4
Estuarine invertebrates.

(a)   *Macoma balthica*
(Baltic tellin)

(b)   *Cerastoderma edule*
(The cockle)

(c)   *Nereis diversicolor*
(The ragworm)

(d)   *Hydrobia ulvae*
(Mud snail) on mud

Plate 5
Estuarine fish and birds.

(a) *Liparis montagui*
(Sea Snail)

(b) *Syngnathus acus*
(Greater Pipefish)

(c) *Pomatoschistus microps* (Goby)

(d) A flock of waders.

Plate 6 Part of the Burleigh chart of the Humber, showing sandbanks and the position and depth in fathoms of the navigation channel (c. 1560).

IV

Life in the Humber

(D) Birds

Anne Goodall

Introduction

1. The Humber as a whole

2. The inner Humber

3. The middle Humber

4. The outer Humber

Introduction

In terms of coastal bird habitats the Humber has very extensive areas of inter-tidal mud and sand; dunes and dune slacks with sea buckthorn *Hippophae rhamnoides* and other scrub; salt- and brackish-water marshes; *Phragmites* reedbeds; freshwater lakes, and some small areas of shingle. Even the built-up and industrial areas around Hull-Paull and Immingham-Grimsby have muddy frontages which provide important wader feeding areas.

With such variety of habitat it is hardly surprising that so much of the estuary is recognised to have high ornithological value. It includes the Wildfowl Refuge, established by Act of Parliament in 1955, a national Bird Observatory at Spurn, RSPB reserves at Blacktoft Sands and Tetney Marshes, and a number of areas managed as private or County Trust reserves. Much of the area of flats and marshes has either already been designated a Site of Special Scientific Interest by the Nature Conservancy Council, or is proposed for notification, while the estuary as a whole fulfils the criteria for designation as a Special Protection Area under the terms of the European Community Directive on the Conservation of Wild Birds, and for inclusion on the list of Wetlands of International Importance under the Ramsar Convention.

In addition, the Saltfleetby-Theddlethorpe National Nature Reserve, though just outside the estuary proper, is firmly linked to it. It provides, for example, wader roosting sites when the highest spring tides flood roosts on both shores at the Humber mouth, sanctuary for the brent geese and shelduck when disturbance is high within the estuary and the major winter roost for hen harriers which hunt over the south shore marshes right up to Humberston.

Despite its obvious importance, the Humber must rank ornithologically as the least-known of Britain's major estuaries, and in large part this is due to the lack of published information on it. Spurn Bird Observatory, Blacktoft Sands Reserve and the Saltfleetby NNR have permanent wardens, while the Wildfowl Refuge and Tetney Reserve have full-time wardens in winter and summer respectively. All of these areas are regularly logged but only the Spurn data are published; counts and observations at the other sites, though made available to the two county bird recorders for use in the Yorkshire and Lincolnshire Bird Reports, are otherwise only reported internally.

There have been a number of amateur studies, some of them long-term, but little of this work is published except as private reports with restricted local circulation. In recent years several studies have also been carried out by the University of Hull with MSC/NCC and other backing. Tasker and Milsom (1979) looked at waders and wildfowl using the lower and upper estuary between February 1978 and March 1979 and August 1978 and February 1979 respectively. The bulk of the fieldwork was carried out on the north bank but some areas of the south shore were visited and some locally available data-sources were tapped. Shepherd *et al.* (1982) studied the Pyewipe mudflats intensively between February 1981 and March 1982. By quantifying especially the feeding numbers both these studies upgraded the known status of many species. Shepherd (1985) was commissioned by the RSPB/NCC to update the Pyewipe observations for the period December 1985 to

January 1986. Collation of information has also been carried out under contract (Goodall, unpublished).

Otherwise the main sources of information are the continuing censuses organised by national ornithological bodies, in particular the BTO/RSPB/NCC 'Birds of Estuaries Enquiry' which has been running since 1968 and more recently the monthly wintering wildfowl counts collected by the Wildfowl Trust.

Both of these require (mainly amateur) observers to count the birds present on a particular stretch of coast (mainly waders) or defined water (mainly wildfowl) on a set day each month, if possible throughout the winter. The two enquiries thus complement each other and are reported jointly each year. Most of the report deals, naturally, with national trends, though for each species the most important estuaries/sites are listed and the Humber appears in many of these lists. Even these tend to underestimate the estuary's importance, since the priority counts take place in mid-winter and many species make their major use of the estuary on passage.

Between them these studies do indicate the intensive use birds make of the Humber. Populations from all over north-west Europe mingle here, stopping off to feed during their migrations, or over-wintering or summering, as juveniles alongside the resident British breeders. Different species exploit the Humber at different times and different sections of the estuary provide for the requirements of particular species. This contribution attempts to summarise the complex information by firstly looking at the estuary as a whole and then examining the three sections into which it can be divided on ornithological grounds.

1. The Humber as a whole

An estuary or water is considered nationally important if it regularly holds either more than 1% of the national population of a particular species or sub-species of waterbird, or a total of 10,000 waders or wildfowl, and internationally important if it holds either more than 1% of the whole population of that species or a total of 20,000 waders or wildfowl (Smart 1976, Spagnesi 1982, Pienkowski 1986). On these criteria the Humber estuary holds nationally important populations of eighteen species, and inter-

85

nationally important populations of eight of these. Table 4.5 lists these species, with the months in which numbers on the Humber exceed the 1% standard.

In addition, the 'summed peak' count (the sum of the highest count of each species, i.e. the absolute minimum of birds using the estuary) for 1983/4, when counts were made monthly from September through to May, gave mid-winter peak (Dec.-Feb.) figures of 16,667 wildfowl and 70,529 waders; the all-year summed peak was 22,127 wildfowl and 91,692 waders. In most years counts are made only in the mid-winter months, so full totals are not available but the 1983/4 count is likely to be typical. The mid-winter peak count for 1984/5 for example was 17,692 wildfowl and 77,257 waders.

These totals put the Humber in fourth place in the national league table, behind the extensive complexes of Morecambe Bay, the Wash and the Ribble/Dee.

In mid-winter the most numerous species using the estuary are dunlin (3.5% of the British population) and knot (up to 10%). Dunlin have been shown to be very faithful to a particular wintering area and their numbers therefore fluctuate little once the wintering population has arrived. Knot on the other hand are much more mobile and hard weather, with freezing of continental estuaries, regularly brings a sudden influx. In many winters flocks of 10,000 or more suddenly arrive on the Humber mudflats.

The same is true of lapwing and golden plover, but neither of these is confined to estuaries and flocks are more likely to arrive on the shore from inland when their traditional feeding areas freeze. A closely related species which does show inter-estuarine mobility is the grey plover. The stable wintering population is quite small (though still some 5% of the British population) but in many years flocks of up to 1000 arrive quite suddenly, stay a short time and then leave.

In mid-winter the shore is also used by flocks of passerines, particularly skylarks and greenfinches but including, too, meadow pipits, reed and corn buntings, yellowhammers, and in the outer Humber, twite and snow buntings. In recent years lapland buntings have been regular visitors but shore larks occur mainly on the north shore; on the south bank they are now rarely seen. These flocks attract raptors and both short-eared owls and hen harriers are found throughout the estuary at this time.

86

	JUL	AUG	SEP	OCT	NOV	DEC	JAN	FEB	MAR	APR	MAY	JUN
Brent Goose	J											
Shelduck			s	O	N	D	J	F	M			
Wigeon					n	d	j	f				
Teal			s		n	d	j	f				
Mallard					n	d	j	f				
Oystercatcher			s	o	n	d	j	f				
Ringed Plover	j	a	s	o	n	d	j	f			m	
Golden Plover			s	o	n	d	j	f				
Grey Plover*		a	s	o	n	d	j	f	m	a	m	
Lapwing					n	d	j					
Knot			s	O	N	D	J	F	M			
Sanderling	J	A	S	O	N	D	J	F	M	A	M	J
Dunlin		a	s	o	n	D	J	f	m	a	m	j
Ruff	j	a	s		n		j					
Bar-tailed Godwit						d	j	f				
Whimbrel	j	a								a	m	
Curlew			s	o	n	d	j	f	m			
Redshank			S	O	N	D	J	F	m			

Key: Upper-case letters denote internationally important populations; lower-case letters nationally important populations
* Grey Plover reach internationally important numbers each year, but in different months (September-February).

Table 4.5 Bird species with populations that regularly reach nationally or internationally important levels in the Humber.

2. The inner Humber

The inner Humber, above the Bridge, holds most of the wildfowl (with one exception, discussed below). The Wildfowl Refuge (Fig. 4.9) was originally established here to provide a protected area for the pink-footed goose, but the numbers of this species have declined steadily from an annual average peak of about 10,000 between 1955 and 1960, to a few hundred in most years now. This decline has been related to changes in Scottish cereal growing, providing winter feed there so that the geese have no need to fly further south (Boyd & Ogilvie 1969). However, the poisoning incident in January 1975 when more than 200 geese died (Hamilton & Stanley 1975) may have speeded up the trend.

Other species present in important numbers include mallard, wigeon, teal and shelduck, while smaller numbers of the other common wildfowl regularly occur. On the north bank the major sites for wildfowl are Brough Sand and Whitton Sand, with south bank concentrations around Read's Island and Winteringham Middle Sand. At the confluence of the Ouse and Trent the lagoons on the Blacktoft Sands reserve provide safe conditions, particularly favoured by teal, and on occasion large flocks of mallard and wigeon also use Alkborough Flats.

Wader numbers in the upper estuary are much lower than those further east, although, particularly at the peak of autumn passage, some 8-10,000 birds may be present. The commonest species using this area are dunlin, lapwing and golden plover with smaller numbers of ringed plover, redshank and curlew. Small parties of black-tailed godwit and whimbrel occur regularly on passage (and the former may summer) and a few oystercatchers are present from February to October when they move up-river to breed, but sanderling and turnstone are rare above the bridge.

Wintering numbers are generally much lower, though hard-weather movements may bring very large flocks of lapwing and golden plover into the estuary and the grazing marshes attract high numbers of snipe at this season.

At low water the feeding birds spread out across the mudflats but concentrate at high water on to Read's Island and Whitton Sand. Until the mid-seventies Alkborough Flats also held a size-able roost but a decrease in cattle-grazing there, together with the provision of shallow lagoons across the Trent at Blacktoft Sands

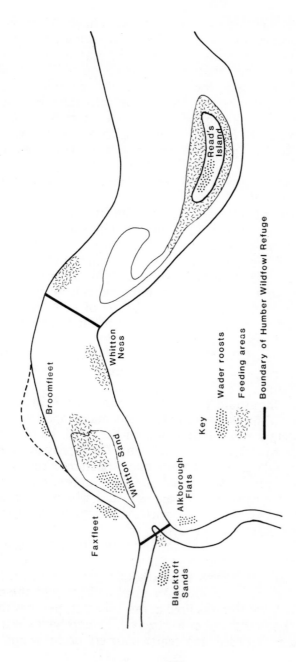

Figure 4.9   The inner Humber showing the main feeding areas and daytime wader roost sites.

and the natural building-up of Whitton Sand have all combined to lessen its importance to waders. However, spring passage flocks still roost there, particularly if wigeon have grazed there in winter or winter storms have flattened the long grass. The Blacktoft lagoons hold a steady roost through the autumn, inversely correlated with tidal height; they come into their own at the equinoctial springs, the only tides which now cover Whitton Sand. Even at low water the lagoons offer good feeding and most of the less common waders, plus occasional national rarities, occur here on passage.

The main wader roosts and feeding areas in this section are shown in Figure 4.9.

Of the other waterbirds using the estuary itself, seabirds are uncommon so far up-river and are generally vagrants sheltering from winter storms. Some parties of skuas and terns, both black and 'commic' (common/arctic) occur on migration, apparently using the Trent and Ouse as flyways, and this inner third of the estuary also holds a large gull roost, building up from July-August to a late autumn peak. Evening flight-lines of gulls can be seen from late summer, moving along the main tributary rivers and the Yorkshire and Lincolnshire Wolds, with the birds concentrating on and in the lee of Redcliff Middle Sand (Shepherd 1983). All four common species are present, with smaller numbers of lesser black-backed gulls.

Two further important habitats are found in this area: freshwater lakes and *Phragmites* reedbeds. The major open waters are the Welton waters and Faxfleet pits on the north bank and the Barton and Barrow clay pits on the south. These provide breeding habitat for Canada geese and many ducks (including ruddy ducks of recent years) plus great crested and little grebes, mute swans, water rails and kingfishers. In autumn and winter the rafts of ducks using these waters include pochard and goldeneye, together with occasional rarer visitors such as smew.

Reedbeds are found both in the old clay pits and fringing the river itself. The most extensive, at Blacktoft Sands, is a special case of the latter. Breeding birds in this habitat include bearded tits, reed warblers and occasionally short-eared owls, though these also use rough grassland. Bitterns bred at one time but, possibly due to disturbance, 'boomers' are now rare. Cetti's and Savi's warblers have both been recorded and marsh harriers occur annually at

90

Blacktoft Sands, though they don't breed every year. In recent years there have been regular sightings at other sites along the Humber also.

In autumn the reedbeds are used as passage roosts by passerine migrants. These include reed and sedge warblers and wagtails, but commonest of all are hirundines, particularly swallows, of which a million or more must pass through in a good year. Juvenile starlings also use these reedbed roosts and later in the winter they are used by finches and buntings, including yellowhammers. Not surprisingly, many raptors take advantage of the passerine flocks; peregrine falcons, hen harriers, merlins, sparrowhawks and kestrels are all regular winter visitors to the Humber banks.

3.   The middle Humber

The Humber's middle section stretches down-stream from the bridge to a line drawn approximately north from Grimsby Docks. On the north shore about half of this is built up and industrialised, with only a narrow strip of mud along its frontage between the bridge and Salt End. The south shore also has an industrial area fronting the river from Grimsby north-west to Killingholme, and apart from the Pyewipe mudflats, there is very little inter-tidal mud along most of this section. Above Killingholme a few waders, mainly dunlin and ringed plover, use the mud, but there is no large roost. On autumn passage some 200-300 small waders roost at Killingholme and a similar number at Goxhill, but most of the other waders fly south-east at high water to the Humber mouth roosts.

From Thorngumbald Drain lighthouse round to Hawkin's Point stretch the Foulholme Sands. These, with the Pyewipe flats immediately north-west of Grimsby Docks, form the main wild-fowl and wader feeding sites in the mid-section and the major grounds on the estuary for curlew and shelduck and possibly also for redshank and dunlin.

Up to a thousand curlew feed on the mud of the Pyewipe flats, crossing the river on most tides to use the main north bank roosts on Cherry Cobb Sands Outstray and the fields around Stone Creek. A second large flock remains on the north bank to feed at low water on Foulholme Sand or inland on grass fields. A smaller

91

flock of some ninety birds is recorded in the Salt End area, with one of similar size at Goxhill on the south shore. As with the Salt End and Stone Creek birds, part of this flock feeds on the mud and the remainder on grass fields inland. To what extent the field- and mud-feeders within a flock interchange is not known and some of the Goxhill mud-feeders probably join those on the fields at high water; however, it seems likely that others cross the river to the roosts opposite.

Shelduck reach their highest density in this section in late autumn/early winter, when more than 3000 birds (about 4% of the British population) are probably feeding on the Pyewipe and Foulholme mud. Unlike the curlews, no apparent cross-river inter- change occurs, the Pyewipe birds roosting on the water locally at high tide and the Foulholme birds doing likewise or moving on to Cherry Cobb Sands Outstray. In summer 1978 a small moulting flock was found to use the outer edge of Foulholme Sands (Tasker 1982), making the Humber the fourth known moulting area in Britain.

Redshank also show little roost interchange, with the Foulholme birds using the same roosts as the curlews and the Pyewipe birds roosting on Courtaulds factory roof, together with most of the Pyewipe dunlin. Dunlin from Foulholme, however, move to the Humber mouth roosts on spring tides, together with the other waders which feed on this area. These include large flocks of knot, particularly in late winter, and smaller numbers of bar-tailed godwits, grey plover and turnstone. The main roost sites in the middle and outer Humber are shown in Figure 4.10a-c.

At one time both banks in this section were backed by fresh- water grazing marsh but though there is still a fair amount of pasture only remnants of the marshes remain. The Killingholme marshes for example are represented now by four pits of varying water-depths around North Killingholme Haven, and 10 hectares of pits and wet grassland some 2-3km south. The great variety of waterbirds and waders recorded here, particularly on passage, illustrates how rich the avifauna of this area must once have been.

Seabirds occur more regularly in this section than they do above the bridge. Gannets and fulmars may be seen on feeding forays in the breeding season as well as when migrating, and north-easterly gales in the North Sea bring many thousands of gulls inside the estuary to sit out the storm.

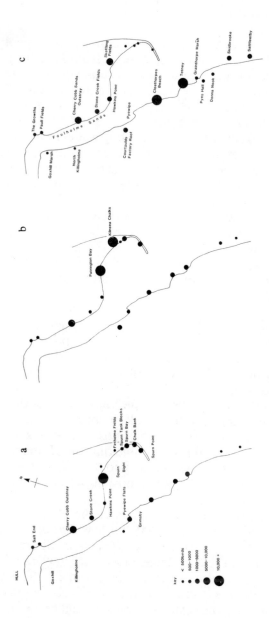

Figure 4.10   The wader roost sites in the middle and outer Humber
(a)   Daytime neap tides.
(b)   Daytime mid-tides.
(c)   Daytime spring tides.

93

4. The outer Humber

The outer Humber comprises Spurn Bight and the Spurn peninsula on the north bank and the shore south-east from Cleethorpes on the south. The section on invertebrates in this volume described the distribution and productivity of invertebrates in Spurn Bight. Figure 4.11 shows a summary of the feeding areas of the principal bird species using this area as recorded by Tasker & Milsom (1979). Most of the inter-tidal area is used by feeding waders when the tide uncovers the flats and each species uses these areas according to its own requirements and feeding method. It is no surprise, however, that the birds are mainly found in the most productive middle and upper shore areas.

Major roosts occur at Patrington, Spurn, Cleethorpes, Tetney and Saltfleet. On spring tides waders from the north shore cross the river to roost, but on the highest springs the south shore roosts are also inundated; under these conditions field roosts may develop or the birds may leave the estuary altogether to roost on the Saltfleetby NNR.

Major species occurring in this section are oystercatcher, knot, grey plover and sanderling, the latter mainly confined to the sandy south shore, with a few on the seaward side of Spurn peninsula. Sanderling are high arctic breeders with a very short breeding season and as little as six weeks between their 'spring' and 'autumn' migrations so that, as Table 4.5 shows, internationally important numbers occur on the Humber in every month of the year. The spring movement, with a peak of some 2500-3000 birds in late May, is particularly significant; most sanderling passage occurs on the west coast, and it is possible that the Humber holds as many birds as the rest of the east and south coasts together at this time. Arguably, the Humber is the most important site for this species on the entire east coast.

In the last decade brent goose numbers at the Humber mouth have increased considerably. Up to 3000 birds winter on the south shore, centred at Saltfleet, with some 200-300 in Spurn Bight. Most of the birds are of the dark-bellied race but a few individuals of the light-bellied race also occur in some winters. The outer Humber also supports a wintering flock of shelduck, but it is not known whether these are the same birds present higher up the river in late autumn, or whether they represent a separate influx from

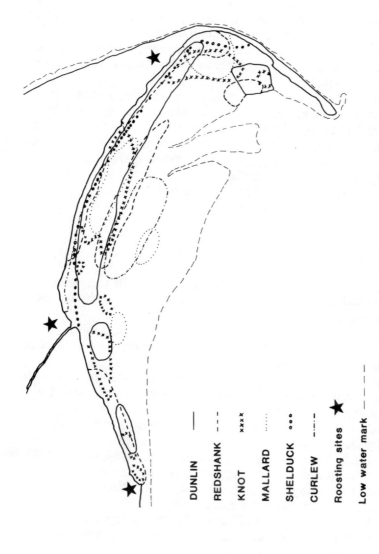

DUNLIN —————

REDSHANK — — —

KNOT ××××

MALLARD ·········

SHELDUCK ∘ ∘ ∘

CURLEW — ·· —

Roosting sites ★

Low water mark — — — —

Figure 4.11   The main feeding areas of some of the commonest birds using Spurn Bight. (Based on Tasker & Milsom, 1979).

the Waddensee after the autumn birds have moved on.

Due to the lack of cliffs or other suitable observation posts, use of the Humber mouth by seabirds, other than those which feed inshore, is certainly under-recorded. Regular sea-watching at Spurn and incidents like the oiling and auk wrecks of 1983 have indicated that fair numbers regularly pass or are present at the mouth. Those that do feed inshore include the terns with attendant skuas, small flocks of eider, common scoter and other seaducks and a regular late winter assembly of divers (mainly red-throated) off Donna Nook.

A final habitat, unique to this outer section, is the fringing barrier of sand dunes and sea buckthorn scrub down the Spurn peninsula and across the river running south from Donna Nook. In summer both shores hold important colonies of little terns; on passage a great variety of passerine and other migrants occur here, including many national rarities, and the dunes also provide a landfall for winter visitors crossing the North Sea.

References

Boyd, H. & Ogilvie, M.A. Changes in the British wintering population of the pink-footed goose from 1950 to 1965. *Wildfowl* 20, 33-46 (1969).

Hamilton, G.A. & Stanley, P.I. Further cases of poisoning of wild geese by an organophosphorus winter wheat seed treatment. *Wildfowl* 26, 49-54 (1975).

Pienkowski, M.W. Qualifying levels for national importance for non-breeding waterfowl. Nature Conservancy Council. Chief Scientist Directorate 1986.

Shepherd, I.G. The nocturnal gull roost census 1983. *Lincolnshire Bird Report* 1983.

Shepherd, I.G. Birds of Pyewipe mudflats Dec. 1984 — Jan. 1985. Unpublished Report to the RSPB and NCC 1985.

Shepherd, I.G., Hayhow, S.J. & Roden, A. Birds of Pyewipe mudflats. Unpublished Report to NCC 1982.

Smart, M. (Ed.) 1976 Proceedings of the international conference on conservation of wetlands and waterfowl, Heiligenhafen FRG 1974. IWRD, Slimbridge.

Spagnesi, M. (Ed.) 1982 Proceedings of the conference on conservation of wetlands of international importance especially as waterfowl habitat. Cagliari 1980. Instituto Nazionale di Bologia della Selvaggina, Bologna.

Tasker, M.L. Moulting shelducks on the Humber. *Bird Study* 29, 164-6 (1982).

Tasker, M. & Milsom, T.P. Birds of the Humber Estuary. Unpublished Report to NCC 1979.

V

Navigation and charting of the Humber

A.M. Ferrar

Introduction

1. Ferry crossings of the Humber

2. Early sea-going traffic

3. Navigation of the Humber

4. Charting of the Humber

5. Navigation aids

Introduction

The Humber has been a barrier to travellers by road, and a highway for travellers by boat for many centuries. The Roman road from Lincoln to York was interrupted by the Humber, and in order to overcome the obstacle a ferry had to be provided from Winteringham to Brough. The ends of this ferry were in two of the many creeks and inlets, which provided shelter for small boats. Others of these little havens were used by fishing boats and when a town began to grow up at the mouth of the River Hull fishermen from both sides of the estuary sold part of their catch to the towns-people. With the passing centuries and growth in population, the markets at Hull became more important, not only to fishermen, but to farmers and traders of all kinds.

1. Ferry crossings of the Humber

On market days boats carried passengers and goods from many small creeks and havens, such as Stallingborough, Goxhill and Barrow, to Hull. In the early nineteenth century these market boats were so numerous that they caused a good deal of congestion at Hull, both in the Old Harbour and along the Humber waterfront. But though they were numerous, and much used by local people, they did not provide a regular service and so did not attract travellers from farther afield. There were, however, several ferries and these provided the only regular public service across the river. The shortest crossings were from Barton to Hessle, and from Winteringham to Brough. From Barton, Barrow and Goxhill there were services to Hull. The Barton to Hull crossing was the longest, being about five miles, and if the weather was bad it could be an unpleasant and dangerous journey, lasting for about four hours, in the small sailing vessels which were used until early in the nineteenth century. But it was the route which attracted most travellers as it provided a direct link between Hull and the stage coach service to London.

The introduction of a small steam vessel in 1821, and improvements in landing facilities, resulted in a more reliable service. The number of daily crossings was also increased from one to two. The London mails, which had previously come via York, were transferred to this route.

The Hull to New Holland ferry was of more recent origin. In the early years of the nineteenth century two men began to ferry passengers to Hull in an open boat, from a small creek near Barrow. On account of its isolated position it was also used by smugglers. The name of New Holland is reputed to have originated from the Hollands gin, brought ashore here by smugglers. Little is known about this service, and it may not have lasted long. In 1825 or 1826 a Barton man, Joseph Brown, recognising that the principal drawback to the Barton-Hull service was its length, bought some land near the Oxmarsh creek in Barrow and proposed to set up a daily ferry service, and to run coaches to London which would connect with it. The company which he formed also built the Yarborough Arms at New Holland for the convenience of the travellers he hoped to attract. At first the ferry was not much used — the Humber crossing was made in a sailing boat and the road approaches to New Holland were so poor that there was delay in establishing a coach service. So it did not provide a very attractive alternative to the Barton service. But in 1832 a small steam boat, the *Magna Carta*, inaugurated a service three times a day in each direction, with an extra journey on market days. Better landing facilities were also constructed at New Holland. Several years of fierce competition between the Barton and New Holland routes now followed and in 1836 the London Mail was transferred to the new route. By 1848 the ferry had come under the control of a railway company and New Holland became the terminus for a branch from the Grimsby to Gainsborough railway line. It was not long before most of the traffic from Hull came by this route, instead of going through Barton. The Barton to Hull crossing fell into decline, though the Barton to Hessle ferry remained active for some time. It was a short crossing, and boats were timed to connect with trains on the Hull to Selby railway. It was also used for cattle and other livestock.

2. Early sea-going traffic

It is clear, however, that in addition to the comings and goings of the ferries the Humber was also used by sea-going vessels from a very early date. Within the last century the buried remains of four large prehistoric boats have been found, three on the North Ferriby foreshore and one at Brigg. The Ferriby boats were found in 1938, 1940 and 1963. Two were partially cleared of silt, the details of their structure were recorded, and they were refilled with silt to protect them from erosion. Later they were lifted and removed and one is now on public exhibition at the Maritime Museum at Greenwich. Several methods of determining their age — by radiocarbon dating, by a study of the mosses and other plant material used to caulk seams between the planks, and also of the fragments of pottery found in association with them — agree in pointing to a date about 1000 BC — the early to middle Bronze Age. The remains were well preserved and sufficiently complete for reliable estimates of the size of the boats to be made; and for details of their structure to be studied. One, at least, was over fifty feet long, and eight or nine feet wide. From its design we know that it could be either rowed or sailed. Though these boats were clearly capable of going to sea we can only speculate about the sort of voyages they undertook.

The next evidence comes in the Norse sagas, and from them it seems that the waterway was used by Viking ships during the ninth and tenth centuries. In 1066 Harald Hardraade, King of Norway, entered the Humber on his way to York, and the Battle of Stamford Bridge, a month or so before the Battle of Hastings.

By 1160 a trading settlement, by the name of Wyke, had grown up at the point where the River Hull flows into the Humber. It belonged to the Abbey of Meaux, situated a little way up the river. In 1299 it was acquired by King Edward I, who re-named it King's Town upon Hull, and granted it its first charter. The principal purpose for which the King wanted it was as a supply base for his wars in Scotland. The sea route was more efficient and reliable than any land route he could have used.

3.   Navigation of the Humber

This was the context in which the Guild of Trinity House was established in 1369. It was a charitable institution with wide interests in the town and at first it laid no particular emphasis on maritime affairs. But, of course, the local shipmasters played a prominent part in it, in their capacity as local residents. Among their preoccupations safe navigation on the Humber, naturally, figured largely. It is a complicated estuary, full of shoals and sand-banks; and as these are sometimes extended, and sometimes cut back by tidal streams the navigation channels shift in position. The detailed knowledge needed to use the waterway safely could only be built up by many years of working upon it. This knowledge was not written down, but transmitted orally from master to apprentice. So it was difficult, and indeed dangerous for strangers to use the estuary without the help of a local man as pilot. In 1512 arrangements were made for the Guild to assign 'good men' to bring ships into port, and in this we can see the beginnings of a pilotage service.

Not long afterwards, in the early sixteenth century, a plan of Hull was drawn, and a copy is available for study in the British Museum (Fig. 5.1). It shows the layout of the houses and gardens, within a strong town wall. The River Hull is full of ships, some of

101

Figure 5.1   Part of a manuscript map of Hull, probably about 1530; showing ships being unloaded by riverside cranes, a chain across the entrance to the River Hull and an artillery battery to defend it.

them being unloaded by cranes on the west bank. The wharves are connected with High Street by stairs, or staithes. The mouth of the river is defended by an artillery battery set up outside the town wall, and it is further protected by a chain used to bar the entrance at night.

The problem of safe navigation has been of greater significance in history than is sometimes realised. As landsmen so many of us look at a map and assume that ships can go anywhere on the sea. We are so accustomed to well-defined roads that we give little thought to route finding, and do not realise the importance of landmarks. We have no instinctive appreciation of the dangers of shallow water, or of the complications introduced by the rise and fall of the tide. In order to bring a ship into port it is crucially important to know where sandbanks and other dangers are situated, and how much water there is over them at any state of the tide. The first essential is to avoid them when it is impossible to pass over them safely. But if, at high tide, it is safe, a great deal of time may be saved by taking a short cut over them. There are also many harbours that it is only possible to enter at high tide, on account of sand bars at their entrances.

Pilots did not normally set their local knowledge down in writing for several reasons, apart from the fact that they were practical sailors and often not literate. It would have been difficult to keep it up-to-date. Changes in the sea bed, leading to displacement of the navigation channel can take place quite quickly. Landmarks, which may be prominent buildings, such as churches, or specially constructed beacons, or even just a distinctive group of trees may disappear; or new ones may be set up. It was also considered necessary to keep it secret. The knowledge was the principal 'stock-in-trade' of the pilot, and the means by which he earned his living. There were, too, good reasons for wishing to keep it from any potential enemy, and disclosure might well be regarded as treasonable. It is worth remembering that as late as the Napoleonic Wars, in the late eighteenth and early nineteenth centuries, the Royal Navy lost more vessels by shipwreck on inadequately chartered coasts, than through enemy action.

4. Charting of the Humber

Apart from a sketch of the Humber, drawn by a military engineer in the reign of Henry VIII, the first chart of the Humber that we know of, which is also the earliest English chart to show water depth by soundings, is a manuscript which belonged to Lord Burleigh, Queen Elizabeth's Secretary of State. It was probably drawn about 1560 and is a beautiful and very interesting document (Plate 6). But nothing was printed until a Dutchman, by the name of Waghenaer, produced an atlas of charts which he called 'The Mariner's Mirror'. These charts cover the north-west coast of Europe from Portugal to southern Scandinavia, and the south and east coasts of Britain. At this time the Dutch monopolised the coasting trade from Lisbon by which the spices and other merchandise brought from the Far East by Portuguese ships were distributed. Waghenaer himself was a pilot, at one of the ports on the Zuider Zee, and it was there that he met most of the people engaged in this trade and collected the information for his charts. The first edition, with text in Dutch, was published in 1584. An English edition, with text translated by Anthony Ashley of the Privy Council, was issued in 1588. The Humber appears on a full-page chart covering the coast from Norfolk to Scarborough. Though quite good it is not nearly detailed enough. The text (in modern English) runs

'. . . And if you will enter the channel of Humber, sail in along the northern point of Spurnhead, because the south side is flat and full of shoals, but being entered a little way, cross to the other side of the river, towards Grimsby, within the shoal, where you may ride (at anchor) in six or seven fathoms. But if you wish to go farther in, up to Hull, keep on west-northwest along by the south side to the end of the shoal; then turn northward into the river. Then you must go west southwest, and west by south . . .'

This too is alright as far as it goes, but it is quite inadequate for a stranger wishing to use the estuary. In spite of its shortcomings, the 'Mariner's Mirror' was very useful. Its popularity was such that for a long time afterwards ordinary sailors referred to any volumes containing charts and sailing directions as 'Waggoners', after its author.

In 1643 William Blaeu, another Dutchman, published the 'Sea

104

Beacon', containing improved charts, and a much more detailed text. But not until John Seller published Book 1 of the 'English Pilot', in 1671, was there a printed chart as detailed as Lord Burleigh's manuscript.

Then, in 1681, Charles II commissioned Captain Greenvile Collins to make a complete survey of the coast of Great Britain. This was the first attempt at systematic survey, as distinct from compilation from the local drawings already in existence. It occupied him for seven years. Of the 120 charts which he produced, forty-eight were engraved and published in 1693 as 'Great Britain's Coasting Pilot'. The Humber estuary occupied the whole of one of these charts and in it we can easily recognise the general shape of the estuary as we know it today. The most obvious difference was that Sunk Island really was an island, quite a small one, surrounded by mudbanks and with a channel quite adequate for small ships between it and the Holderness shore. This was the heyday of the havens of Patrington and Ottringham, and Hedon Haven was still important. There were at least fourteen editions of the 'Coasting Pilot', the last in 1792. But though the position of sandbanks was shown on this chart, they could not be seen, except at low tide. It was only by careful use of a combination of landmarks and seamarks that a ship's master could find his way along the navigation channel. This was a problem which greatly exercised the minds of the members of Trinity House. At no little difficulty and expense they provided buoys as sea marks, repaired them when they suffered damage in storms, and moved them as necessary when the navigation channel shifted. They also took an interest in landmarks, sometimes contributing to the cost of repairing or painting conspicuous buildings.

John Scott's chart of the Humber published in 1734 is interesting for several reasons. It is the first to show the upper Humber, from Hull to Trent Falls. It marks buoys and leading lines, and includes useful sailing directions in a substantial panel of text at the foot of the chart. Leading lines provide, perhaps, the best means of steering an accurate course in coastal waters. The method is to find two markers (landmarks or seamarks) which lie in the same straight line as the course it is desired the ship should follow. If the helmsman then keeps these two markers in coincidence with each other he knows precisely the line along which he is moving. If they appear to drift apart he knows he is off course.

Sometimes, it is possible to follow one leading line until it crosses another, pointing in a different direction. The crossing point gives a very accurate fix of the ship's position.

Other charts followed, including one by William Bligh in 1805. Bligh is popularly known for his involvement in the mutiny on HMS *Bounty* when he attempted to take breadfruit plants from a Pacific island to the West Indies. He was a stern disciplinarian, but he was also an able hydrographical surveyor. Unfortunately, his work on the Humber was hasty and incomplete, as he was called away on other duties. His chart is one of the last to show Sunk Island as an island. By about 1820, when the field work for the Ordnance Survey's first one inch to the mile map of the area was done, the channel to the north of it was reclaimed land and the creeks between Paull and Patrington were cut off from the sea, except for Stone Creek at the western end of the old channel, and Patrington at the eastern end which could still be reached by small boats. But ship sizes were increasing, trade continued to move away from the small harbours to the larger ports, and more detailed charts were needed.

John Hall, a senior member, and later Warden, of Trinity House prepared a chart of the lower Humber from surveys made in 1821 and 1822 and editions corrected to show changes in the hydrography and in navigation aids (such as buoys and beacons) were published at various dates during the next thirty years. In 1828, when Goole was being developed as a port he was largely responsible for organising a survey of the upper Humber. The resulting chart, published in the same year, shows havens and ferries; marks water depth in fathoms below Hessle, and in feet above; and a warning about tidal conditions and the possibility of changes in the shipping channel is included in a lengthy note on the face of the chart.

By this time not only had the Ordnance Survey produced a good map of the land around the Humber, providing for the first time an accurate framework for surveys in the estuary, but a Hydrographic Office had been set up by the Admiralty, which gradually took over responsibility for chart production from the private publishers. In 1823 Captain Hewett in HMS *Fairy* made a more detailed survey of the estuary than any that had yet been attempted. His work marks the arrival on the Humber of standards of accuracy comparable to those which are accepted today. They were the culmination of technical developments begun by Murdoch Mackenzie who began work on his chart of the Orkney Islands in the mid-eighteenth century. It is not particularly difficult to measure the depth of water at any given point, though care must be taken to allow for tidal variations. The difficulty lies in fixing accurately the position of such measurements (known as soundings). It is this position-fixing aspect of the survey which makes a good framework of landmarks so important. In addition, sailing ships are very much at the mercy of constantly changing winds. In order to make good a predetermined course they may have to tack backwards and forwards across it. As they do so the leadsman makes soundings with the lead-and-line, which is basically a weight on a long rope. It is the oldest of the surveyor's instruments and has not changed significantly in two thousand years. When properly handled it can give measurements as accurate as any modern electronic apparatus. But it cannot do so as quickly, so soundings are spaced out along the ship's course, and in order to plot them on the chart each one must be fixed by compass bearings to at least two reliable landmarks; or sextant angles to three landmarks. Work in shallow water, or close inshore could be done in small boats, which can be rowed on more predictable courses. So they were much used for detailed work around sandbanks and other obstacles. With the arrival of steam power closer control was obtained over the courses of larger ships and it then became possible to adopt the modern hydrographic surveyor's practice of running numerous straight lines of soundings, parallel to each other, across the whole of the area being charted. This gives a dense network of depth figures, not all of which appear on the published chart. But they are all needed for the simple reason that it is not possible to look at the sea bed and perceive at a glance where the highest or the lowest points lie. The high points are the points where a ship may go aground, so it is important to find them. The denser the network of soundings the more likely it is that they will be found. A selection is then made for publication, including all the shallow areas, a representative sample of the soundings in navigation channels and other areas likely to be used by shipping; and perhaps a few of the deepest, though to the practical seaman these have little more than curiosity value.

It was at this stage in the evolution of survey methods that the

Hydrographic Office took up its responsibilities. So it came about that new charts were much more accurate, and much more detailed. In fact a great deal of chart work done in the early nineteenth century on rocky coasts which, unlike the Humber with its sandbanks, do not alter with the passing years, remains valid today. But the bed of the Humber is constantly changing, and as it does so the navigation channel shifts, and alters in depth.

Captain Hewett was followed by Captain Calver who, in 1851, charted the lower Humber, from Hull to the sea, and in 1861 the upper Humber. The lower Humber was covered again by Commander Parsons in 1875, by Captain Richards in 1899-1900 and by Captain Simpson in 1909-1910. There was another Admiralty survey in 1914; and in 1936 the first survey in which an echo-sounder was used instead of lead-lines, was made. The echo-sounder measures depth by the time taken for a sound-pulse to go from the survey-ship to the sea bed and back. It is very rapid and labour-saving, so measurements can be taken much closer together. There were further Admiralty surveys in 1946 and in 1959-60. The upper Humber was also surveyed periodically, at first by the Admiralty, but later by the Humber Conservancy Board. In 1966 the Conservancy Board, which by that time was surveying the upper Humber annually, extended its responsibilities to cover the lower Humber.

At the present time Associated British Ports publishes a chart of the lower Humber (from the Humber Bridge to the sea) annually, and of the upper Humber once every two months. These are based on a complete survey of the estuary once a year, with much more frequent partial surveys. The navigation channel in the upper Humber is surveyed every fortnight. In the lower Humber the channel and areas subject to rapid change are covered with comparable frequency. The chart incorporates the latest information available when it is published. Between editions important changes are published, as Notices to Mariners, so every owner can keep his chart up-to-date. When charts are purchased the agents who sell them correct them in accordance with Notices to Mariners issued up to a few days before they are sold.

5. Navigation aids

To conclude this review, it would probably be useful to return briefly to the subject of navigation aids and the part played by Trinity House in providing them. More than a century before the first provision of a navigation aid by Trinity House is mentioned in its records, there was a scheme to build a lighthouse at Spurn. In 1427 Parliament approved a proposal by Reedbarrow to build one, though whether it was ever completed we do not know. We have good reason to believe that the Spurn peninsula itself was washed away about 1600, so Reedbarrow's lighthouse, if it then existed, must have gone too. The peninsula began to re-grow from the southern tip of Holderness at once, and it and the shallow water near it needed to be marked. So in 1674 Justinian Angell built both a high lighthouse, on the top of the new Spurn, and a low one near the shoreline on the seaward side. The two lights provided a leading line, as has already been explained. Being close to the shore-line the low light was vulnerable to storm damage. It had to be rebuilt six times; each time in a different position, on account of the growth of Spurn. A hundred years later it had grown so much that new lighthouses were needed. They were built by Smeaton in 1776 about a mile south of Angell's site. In the course of the next hundred years Smeaton's low lighthouse was rebuilt seven times. His high lighthouse remained in use until the present lighthouse was completed in 1895, and was then demolished.

The first markers set by Trinity House to aid sailors were beacons — wooden structures, set up on the Humber bank, of characteristic shape and easily recognised from a distance (Fig. 5.2). Modern beacons can be seen from the riverside footpath, or the railway line. But it was not long before a need was felt to set markers in the river itself, to mark points where sandbanks lay close to the navigation channel and changes of course would have to be made by the helmsman. In 1585 Trinity House was granted the right to buoy the river, and levy a charge on ships, to meet the cost of doing so. Buoys were frequently damaged, or broken adrift, by bad weather, or by collision with ships. Repairs and resetting were constant sources of expense. They also had often to be moved on account of changes in sandbanks and channels. In 1753 there were buoys at the Bull, Cleeness, Burcom Sand, Middle Sand, Foul Holme Sand, White Booth Roads and the New Sand

Clee Ness Beacon

Donna Nook Beacon

Figure 5.2   Some of the beacons used on the Humber. (From Storey, 1971).

(outside Spurn). For more than two hundred years Trinity House concentrated on marking the outer end of the Humber. Above Hull ships still depended entirely on the skill of the Pilots. In the second quarter of the nineteenth century they began occasionally to lend buoys for marking wrecks and other dangers, but not until 1860 did they accept responsibility for marking the upper Humber.

At night sailing ships did not normally continue on their way, except in the open sea. In coastal waters they anchored until daylight returned. Not so steam ships, which could hold a compass course without having to tack for the wind. So as the numbers of steam ships increased the need for lighted navigation marks was felt. The first lightship was moored at the New Sand for about nine months in 1820. It was a hired vessel, temporarily fitted with a lantern, as an experiment. Then there was a gap until a purpose-built lightvessel was moored at the south end of the Bull Sand early in 1833.

Additional lighthouses were also built; those at Spurn served ships passing along the coast, more than those entering the Humber. They included one at Paull, one at Salt End, two at Killingholme (a high light, and a low light, providing a leading

110

line) and two at Thorngumbald (Fig. 5.3). Early lighthouses depended for their light on coal fires in iron firebaskets which could be hoisted to a suitable height on a pole or a tower. Later, oil was used as fuel for the lamps. In either case it was necessary for someone to be there to tend the light. In the latter part of the nineteenth century gas lamps, which would burn unattended for weeks or months became available. In 1879 one was fitted to a buoy and moored in the Humber. It proved to be not sufficiently robust to withstand the strong tidal currents. But improvements were made and before the end of the century lighted buoys were an established feature. Another improvement introduced in 1886 was a bell buoy, which was valuable in foggy weather. The bell, mounted at the top of the buoy, sounded as it was rocked by water movements.

On modern charts a considerable array of buoys, beacons, lights and other aids to navigation is marked in addition to the basic information on water depth, tides and dangers (such as wrecks and sandbanks). Whenever a buoy is moved, or any other important change takes place, a Notice to Mariners is issued.

High   **Lower**
Killingholme Lighthouses

Paull Lighthouse

Figure 5.3   Lighthouses of the middle Humber. (From Storey, 1971).

References

De Boer, G. *A History of the Spurn Lighthouses*. East Yorkshire Local History Series no. 24. 1968.

De Boer, G. and R.A. Skelton. The Earliest English chart with soundings. *Imago Mundi* vol. 23. 1969.

Storey, A. *Trinity House of Kingston upon Hull*. 1967.

Storey, A. *Hull Trinity House History of Pilotage and Navigational Aids of the River Humber (1512-1908)*. 1971.

VI

The Humber Bridge — lame duck or golden goose?

J. North

Introduction

1. The historically conflicting roles of the Humber Estuary

2. The campaign for a Humber crossing, 1850-1981
   (i)   Proposed Humber rail crossing, 1850-1914
   (ii) Unsuccessful lobbying for a road bridge, 1930-mid 1960s
   (iii) A dramatic about-turn; the events of the late 1960s
   (iv) Further setbacks; the construction phase 1972-81

3. The Humber Bridge in operation, 1981-87

4. The impact of the Humber Bridge

Introduction

The Humber Road Bridge, linking North and South Humberside some eight kilometres to the west of Hull (Fig. 6.1) was opened to traffic in June 1981 amid much debate over its need, cost and financial prospects. Six years later controversy still rages, fuelled by the comparatively high bridge tolls, by arguably disappointing traffic levels, and chiefly by a seemingly desperate financial situation of steadily mounting bridge debts. Those critics who labelled the bridge 'a white elephant' and 'the bridge from nowhere to nowhere', even before it was built, now contend that initial traffic and revenue statistics have merely vindicated their long-held view that there was no economic justification for a Humber Bridge. However, others see the bridge as a vital infra-structural investment which could help to unleash the undoubted

113

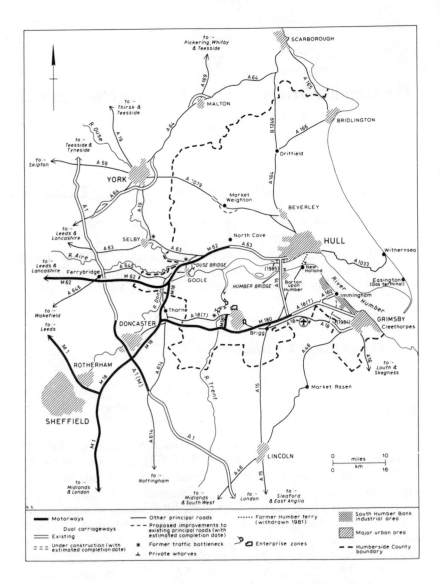

Figure 6.1   The Humber Bridge in its regional setting.

economic development potential of Humberside, described by Lewis and Jones in 1970 as 'a nascent industrial region'. It has been argued that preoccupation with direct and easily quantifiable financial and commercial matters has obscured consideration of the many less tangible but potentially more significant indirect benefits attributable, at least in part, to the bridge. These indirect benefits, which do not appear in the financial returns for the bridge itself, include savings in time, cost and distance both to firms and to individuals plus the stimulus to industrial development and tourism.

To understand the continuing debate over the Humber Bridge, it is essential to know something of its history. This contribution therefore begins by reviewing the protracted and complex saga of the Humber crossing issue, focusing special attention upon the events of the late 1960s which finally precipitated Government approval for the bridge. This is followed by an assessment of the direct and indirect effects of the Humber Bridge in operation during the period 1981-87, with reference to both the local and regional contexts.

1. The historically conflicting roles of the Humber Estuary

The Humber estuary has been one of Britain's principal commercial waterways since medieval times. Its favourable east coast location encouraged short-sea trading connections with western and especially northern Europe, while its navigable tributaries, such as the rivers Ouse and Trent, later augmented by canals in the nineteenth century, provided effective internal links with the industrial areas of northern and midland England (North, 1978). These basic locational advantages, plus the Humber's deep, if variable, navigable channel and an abundance of flat land alongside the estuary, assisted the growth of the ports of Hull, Grimsby, Goole and, more recently, Immingham.

Until 1981, however, the Humber, which varied in width from two kilometres in the vicinity of Hessle to over five kilometres further downstream towards Grimsby, also presented a severe physical barrier to land transport. This barrier had hampered movement between North and South Humberside and had hindered plans for the complementary economic development of

115

these two historically separate sub-regions. The only regular cross-Humber links had been provided by successive generations of ferries which had operated mainly between Hull and New Holland. In modern times these ferries were an anachronism, carrying only twenty cars or light vans on each crossing. Heavy goods vehicles were forced to make an eighty kilometre detour from Hull via Goole in order to reach a point only five kilometres distant across the estuary.

Inevitably both North and South Humberside exhibited an east-west orientation in their transport patterns. The isolation of these areas from each other was both physical and mental, for lack of contact bred mutual feelings of indifference, suspicion and occasionally hostility between their inhabitants. The divergent and sometimes conflicting interests of the North and South Humbersiders were evident throughout the long history of the Humber crossing issue, and indeed contributed to the downfall of some earlier crossing projects.

2. The campaign for a Humber crossing, 1850-1981

Local interests had campaigned for a Humber crossing for over one hundred years. The history of the crossing issue can be divided into four principal phases:-

(i) Proposed Humber rail crossing, 1850-1914

Between 1850 and 1914 efforts by the Hull business community to procure improved rail access for their port led to the promotion of several ambitious schemes which incorporated plans for multiple-span bridges or tunnels across the Humber. This quest for additional rail links intensified once the rationalisation of railway company operations north of the Humber had led to the formation of the North Eastern Railway (NER) in 1854. This new company immediately gained a monopoly of rail traffic to and from Hull. Local merchants believed that the NER's traffic charges and policies discriminated against Hull and in favour of rival East Coast ports such as Hartlepool. Some of these fears were groundless (Brooke, 1972), but the bitter relations between Hull businessmen and the NER prompted concerted attempts to

116

establish independent rail outlets, with the cross-Humber route offering an obvious possible alternative.

Plans for a 'lofty viaduct, about a mile and a half in length' were included in the Hull, Lancashire & Midland Counties Railway project of 1865. This aimed to give Hull more direct access to the Yorkshire coalfield via the Manchester, Sheffield & Lincolnshire Railway (MS & L) system to the south of the estuary. The scheme was short-lived, for neither Hull merchants nor the MS & L would give sufficient financial backing. In sharp contrast, the Hull South & West Junction Railway scheme of 1872-3 gained widespread local support, especially in Hull. It planned to link Hull with the MS & L at Brigg to create a shorter route to London and better access to the steadily expanding Yorkshire, Nottinghamshire and Derbyshire coalfields. A rail tunnel, costing an estimated £340,000 was to have been driven under the Humber between Barton and Hessle. The scheme was submitted to Parliament in 1873 and was approved by a House of Commons Select Committee, but was later rejected by a similar Committee of the House of Lords, reputedly by a single vote.

Before Hull finally gained its independent rail outlet with the opening of the coal-carrying Hull & Barnsley Railway in 1885 another Humber crossing scheme had foundered. The Hull & Lincoln Railway project of 1883 had proposed to cross the estuary, again between Hessle and Barton, by means of a multiple-span bridge costing an estimated £532,000. This scheme was also rejected by Parliament in 1883.

Several factors contributed to the failure of these early Humber crossing proposals. First, the promoters were unable to present conclusive evidence of the engineering feasibility of their respective projects. Secondly, each scheme encountered vehement opposition from highly influential river nagivation interests, who were concerned lest any engineering works in the Humber might adversely affect the notoriously unstable river channels, thereby threatening the future of smaller ports, such as Goole, which lay upstream from the proposed crossing. Equally significant was the concerted opposition from established railway companies, in particular the NER. Inadequate financial backing and a general lack of interest beyond the boundary of Hull were other contributory factors.

Once Hull had achieved its independent rail outlet in 1885 interest in the Humber crossing waned, although it was briefly revived between 1910 and 1913 while railway and dock developments designed to cater for coal exports were being undertaken at Immingham near to Grimsby. When the crossing issue was next raised seriously in the late 1920s, however, the growth in road transport had led to a shift in local opinion in favour of a road crossing scheme.

(ii) Unsuccessful lobbying for a road bridge, 1930-mid 1960s

In 1929, conscious of the growing inadequacy of the Humber ferry service, Kingston upon Hull Corporation commissioned Sir Douglas Fox and Partners, a firm of engineering consultants, to advise on the Humber crossing issue. The Fox Report, published in 1930, advocated the construction of a Humber road bridge on economic, engineering and environmental grounds and recommended the Hessle-Barton site as the preferred location. The report also included specific proposals for a road bridge comprising a principal cantilever section to span the navigable river channel plus twenty-two smaller side spans. The Government promised a seventy-five per cent grant towards the estimated £1.7m costs for the project in an attempt to alleviate high unemployment, and a Humber Bridge Bill was successfully promoted in Parliament. Unfortunately the 1931 financial crisis forced the Government to withdraw the promised grant and the scheme was lost.

The 1931 Humber Bridge Bill was significant for two contrasting reasons. First, it gained widespread acceptance of the engineering feasibility of a Humber Bridge project. Secondly, and less happily, the economic case for building a bridge was based on the grounds that a Humber Bridge could eventually form part of a new and more direct trunk route between London and Newcastle. As Appleton (1966) has demonstrated, this notion was based on a fundamental geographical misconception, since a direct route between these two cities would pass some distance west of the Humber estuary. Nevertheless, Humberside interests persisted with these arguments for the next thirty years. Government Ministers rightly maintained that a Humber Bridge was of regional rather than national importance and therefore of lesser priority than crossings for the Severn, Mersey and Forth estuaries. Accordingly, little forward progress was made towards gaining approval for a Humber Bridge between 1931 and the mid-1960s.

Two developments during this period are, nevertheless, worthy of note. Advances in engineering design and technology resulted in the evolution of plans for a Humber suspension bridge from 1935 onwards. This development seriously undermined opposition to a bridge from river navigation interests. Secondly, a combined initiative from Humberside local authorities in the late 1950s led to the passing of a Humber Bridge Act in 1959. This Act of Parliament set up a Humber Bridge Board, comprising represent- atives of supporting local authorities, which was empowered to borrow money, to acquire the necessary land, to build the bridge and subsequently to levy tolls on traffic. But Government approval and financial support were still withheld. Moreover, support for a Humber Bridge was not universal even locally; south bank authorities, notably Grimsby, argued that improved east- west communications were needed more urgently than a bridge. Meanwhile the estimated cost of building the Humber Bridge had risen from £2.5 million in 1935 to over £13 million by the early 1960s.

(iii) A dramatic about-turn; the events of the late 1960s

Prospects of an early completion for a Humber Bridge seemed to have receded during the mid-1960s. Indeed, in 1965 the Govern- ment approved the construction of new east-west roads to link both North and South Humberside more effectively to the national road network. These roads, which were designed to cater for the principal flows of traffic to and from Humberside, included provision for a toll-free high level crossing of the River Ouse only twenty miles west of the proposed site for a Humber Bridge. No reference was made to a Humber Bridge and Govern- ment opinion on this issue appeared to preclude swift progress.

Within a few months, however, a number of political and socio- economic factors had combined to induce a sudden and dramatic reversal of Government opinion. Approval to build a Humber Bridge was given by the end of the decade. It is argued that the decision was affected by political expediency in relation to a vital Parliamentary by-election in the North Hull Constituency during 1966, (Evans, in Turner 1981), but contemporary socio-economic trends presented equally valid reasons for the change in

Government attitude. National population forecasts had predicted that Britain's population would increase from 56 millions to 75 millions by 2010, creating an urgent need to identify locations capable of accommodating major population and industrial growth outside the principal conurbations. Moreover, prevailing planning opinion favoured a strategy of directing new industrial development towards deep-water estuaries where imported raw materials could be processed more cheaply (James *et al.* 1961). The Humberside Feasibility Study (1969) duly confirmed the physical potential of the spacious, under-utilised Humberside region to accommodate significant population growth and also underlined the suitability of the estuary as a focus for a future Maritime Industrial Development Area. The Study stressed the need to remove the 'divisive effect of the Humber estuary' in order to assist such developments, and therefore recommended construction of the Humber Bridge and its associated link roads as a priority.

The Government, however, still refused to pay for a Humber Bridge, and a further two years elapsed before it finally agreed a loan of seventy-five per cent of total construction costs, then estimated to be £26 million. The remaining loans, plus associated interest charges, had to be repaid from toll revenues within sixty years of the bridge opening, although loan repayments could be suspended for up to thirteen years if revenue was insufficient. The ultimate financial responsibility for the bridge could eventually pass to its guarantors, the ratepayers of the Hull and Beverley Districts on North Humberside and those of Glanford on the south bank.

The most striking feature of the long campaign for a Humber crossing was that all the major initiatives came from north of the river, chiefly from Hull. This was not unduly surprising because Hull, with the largest population and the widest range of service activities on Humberside, has always stood to gain most from a physical link across the estuary. General acceptance of this fact locally has perhaps explained the rather indifferent attitudes shown by south bank authorities and their reluctance to accept financial responsibilities for a crossing (Bowman, 1966; Ward, 1967).

(iv) Further setbacks; the construction phase 1972-81

Even during its construction, further setbacks beset the seemingly ill-fated Humber Bridge. Delays attributable to poor labour relations, to adverse weather conditions, and principally to engineering problems encountered in sinking foundations for the southern tower pier in the estuary itself, all extended the construction phase from five to nine years. Meanwhile the unprecedented inflation of the 1970s produced a massive escalation in construction costs to over £91 million, almost four times the original estimate. The addition of high loan charges brought the total debt of the bridge on opening to approximately £130 million.

The 1970s also witnessed the rapid disappearance of the favourable socio-economic trends of the previous decade. National population forecasts were dramatically reduced as changing socio-economic behaviour brought declining birth rates. Thus Humberside was not required to cater for major population expansion. Reduced prospects for national economic growth led to the scrapping of plans for Maritime Industrial Development Areas. By the early 1980s recession had severely dented the Humberside economy, especially the Scunthorpe steel industry and the fishing industries of Hull and Grimsby, thereby reducing travel demands from both local firms and individuals.

Finally, the delayed completion of the Humber Bridge ensured the prior opening of the east-west motorways linking North and South Humberside respectively to the national motorway network. The M62 Hull-Leeds-Liverpool motorway, with its toll-free Ouse river crossing, opened in 1976, and the M18 links between M62 and the A1 and M1 routes in South Yorkshire in 1978. On South Humberside the M180 with its new Trent crossing was extended to Brigg by 1980. Inevitably, long-distance traffic moving to and from Humberside became accustomed to using these high-speed toll-free routes long before the bridge opened.

These factors led experts to revise drastically estimates of likely Humber Bridge traffic. Optimistic forecasts of 24,000 vehicles per day (vpd) crossing the bridge which were made in the early 1970s had been slashed to a mere 4000 vpd by 1981. Thus the Humber Bridge Board faced an impossible dilemma; tolls had to be sufficiently high to ensure repayment of bridge debts within sixty years, yet low enough to deter traffic from using alternative routes

Table 6.1

Humber Bridge Toll Charges

Tolls per single crossing

	June 1981 £	January 1986 £	January 1988 £
Motor Cycles	0-50p.	0-60p.	0-70p.
Cars/Light Vans	1-00p.	1-20p.	1-50p.
Heavy Commercial Vehicles			
— 2 axle	4-50p.	5-20p.	5-20p.
— 3 axles	6-00p.	6-60p.	6-60p.
— 4 axles	7-50p.	8-00p.	8-00p.
Light Commercial/ Mini Buses	2-00p.	2-40p.	2-90p.
Coaches	4-50p.	5-20p.	5-20p.

(Halcrow Fox, 1977).

Initial toll charges for the Humber Bridge ranged from £1 for private cars to £7.50 for the largest heavy goods vehicles per single crossing (Table 6.1). The next most expensive tolled estuary crossing in Britain had an average toll only one-third of that for the Humber (Freight Transport Association, 1982).

3. The Humber Bridge in operation, 1981-87

The opening of the Humber Bridge and the associated discontinuation of the Humber ferry in 1981 had an immediate effect upon spatial relationships and accessibility levels within Humberside. Overnight Hull and Grimsby, previously 135 kilometres apart by road for goods vehicles, were brought within 65 kilometres of each other, while the Hull-Scunthorpe journey was reduced from 85 kilometres to a mere 32 kilometres. A new

A15 Humber Bridge-Brigg road became the main link between North and South Humberside, leaving the former ferry terminus of New Holland less accessible and much less significant in the regional transport pattern.

Not surprisingly the Humber Bridge attracted extremely high volumes of novelty and sightseeing traffic, with flows occasionally exceeding 20,000 crossings per day. Unfortunately this 'honeymoon period' was short-lived, and traffic levels began to stabilise in the range 6000-10,000 daily crossings. By 1987 weekday traffic averaged 10,200 vpd, with over eighty-one per cent of total crossings made by private cars. However, heavy goods vehicle (HGV) traffic has shown a steady increase from around 3500 crossings per week initially to 7400 per week in 1987. Thus, although HGV traffic accounts for only ten per cent of total bridge crossings, it provides nearly forty per cent of toll revenues.

Table 6.2 summarises the traffic and revenue statistics for the Humber Bridge since June 1981. The Humber Bridge Board was left with an operating surplus (toll revenues minus operating and maintenance costs) in each financial year. Unfortunately in each case this surplus was more than offset by annual interest charges on the original loans. Thus in 1985-6 for example, the operating surplus of £4 million was swamped by an annual interest charge of over £20 million, adding substantially to the overall bridge debt. By mid-1987 the bridge had total debts of more than £275 million and there was little prospect of a slowing in the rate of increase of the debt given present traffic levels. Efforts to persuade central Government to write off the bridge debt had yielded little positive response. In 1986, therefore, the Humber Bridge Board had been forced to increase toll charges for the first time, by 20 per cent for private cars and by between 5 and 15 per cent for goods vehicles (Table 6.1).

The composition and origin-destination patterns of Humber Bridge traffic are of particular interest in the context of the tolls issue. Traffic data have been compiled from a variety of sources. Comprehensive interview surveys were conducted on the Humber Bridge in May 1982 and May 1986 (Humberside County Council, 1982, 1986). Additional analysis of pre-paid ticket sales to industrial and commercial firms (North, 1984) has helped to identify many regular bridge users. Finally, a sample survey of 200 firms located in an area bounded by Teesside, York, Nottingham

Table 6.2 Humber Bridge: Traffic and Revenue 1981-87

a) Vehicle Crossings

Vehicle Class	1981-2*	1982-3	1983-4	1984-5	1985-6	1986-7
Motor Cycles	50,734	58,918	53,918	55,483	56,068	51,469
Cars and Light Vans	1,904,508	2,217,326	2,325,347	2,568,543	2,787,793	3,016,305
Cars and Light Vans with Trailers	23,261	32,538	33,587	34,724	35,144	34,475
Heavy Commercial						
— 2 axle	63,822	102,204	124,056	145,666	147,299	154,771
— 3 axle	24,176	31,699	33,839	39,016	37,305	35,774
— 4 axle	90,553	138,243	148,473	158,460	166,137	195,970
Light Commercial/ Mini Buses	35,338	49,507	46,437	54,456	46,859	115,569
Coaches	13,735	16,655	14,622	14,520	17,061	34,358
Exempt traffic and service buses	71,360	81,577	82,013	101,038	88,823	85,438
TOTAL	2,277,487	2,726,270	2,862,292	3,171,906	3,398,995	3,724,129

* June 3 1981 to March 31 1982 only

b) Revenue

	1982-3 £	1983-4 £	1984-5 £	1985-6 £	1986-7 £
	4,143,464	4,476,193	4,810,129	5,350,985	6,589,507

Source: Humber Bridge Board

and East Anglia (North, 1984) yielded information about the frequency and purpose of bridge journeys, plus an indication of responses to the opening of the bridge.

The May 1982 traffic survey confirmed the essentially local role of the Humber Bridge during its first year of operation. Sixty-five per cent of total crossings were for journeys which began and ended in Humberside. A further thirty per cent of traffic either began or ended its journey within the county. Only five per cent of traffic was involved in through journeys which started and finished beyond Humberside with less than two per cent overall comprising journeys from beyond Lincolnshire to and from York and beyond. HGV traffic showed a higher proportion of non-Humberside journeys (30%), but average trip length for all journeys in May 1982 was 72 kilometres, with a median value of 53 kilometres. Levels of toll charges, especially for heavy goods vehicles, were undoubtedly significant in deterring long distance traffic but the limited capacity of the A15 Brigg-Lincoln and A1079 Hull-York roads to the south and north of the estuary respectively has also been a contributory factor. By 1982, however, some firms had not fully adjusted to the bridge opening and had not revised operating schedules.

Data from all three surveys were used to identify the principal commercial traffics using the Humber Bridge. Bulk traffics are especially important and are dominated by the distribution of fuel oils and petro-chemical products from the industrial plants of the South Humber Bank area. Some firms now operate a shuttle service, with fleets of tankers making upwards of twenty round trips across the bridge each day. However, for longer journeys, for example between Immingham and Teesside, tankers still use the faster, toll-free M180-M62-A1 route. Other bulk traffics include cement and allied building materials moving from factories in South Humberside to builders' merchants and other retail outlets on the North Bank, and imported timber which is distributed from stockists in Hull to South Humberside. An important if irregular bulk traffic has been the movement of grain from stores in Lincolnshire and East Anglia to the major export terminal at Hull Docks. A highly intensive and seasonal bridge traffic has been the movement of field vegetables such as peas and sprouts direct from farms to processing plants on the opposite bank of the estuary; here the time savings achieved by the Humber Bridge have been crucial in maintaining the quality of harvested crops.

The distribution of food and drink is yet another important element of Humber Bridge traffic. Fish movements are complex, including transfers between the Hull and Grimsby markets to satisfy demand, transfers between these markets and fish processing plants on either side of the estuary, and also movements of fish landed at Scottish and other East Coast ports such as Bridlington to the Grimsby market.

The origin-destination patterns for these principal bridge traffics show a marked emphasis upon journeys between the Greater Hull and Grimsby-Immingham areas, with a secondary Hull-Scunthorpe axis also evident. A majority of the firms interviewed early in 1984 stressed that time savings were of most importance, since these often permitted the completion of two daily return journeys per vehicle compared with a single trip during the pre-bridge era. Greater efficiency in the use of both vehicles and personnel has undoubtedly proved one of the principal benefits which have accrued to local firms.

4. The impact of the Humber Bridge

In assessing the impact of the Humber Bridge it is possible to identify specific responses by industrial and commercial organisations located either within Humberside or beyond the region. But the analysis must also be extended to consider less obvious, yet potentially significant, effects of the bridge's opening. In the latter context, it is important to extend the perspective to incorporate discussion of the role of the Humber Bridge in the future of the region.

Direct responses by firms to the opening of the Humber Bridge have varied enormously. Some companies rationalised their Humberside operations either just before or soon after the bridge opened. For example some companies closed pre-existing distribution depots on North Humberside and concentrated their activities on the south bank, making daily deliveries over the bridge to north bank customers. Substantial cost savings have been achieved despite heavy expenditure (up to £30,000 annually for certain firms) on bridge tolls. Greater flexibility of vehicle operation has also benefitted local haulage firms, who can now transfer lorries, trailers and containers between the Humber ports more easily as demand arises. Many existing firms have been able to extend their sales areas to include the opposite bank of the Humber and local contractors have been able to tender more competitively for jobs across the river.

There is some, admittedly limited, evidence of new firms being attracted to Humberside at least in part by the opportunities provided by the bridge. These include a number of companies engaged in service activities which could help to diversify the region's economic base. Overall the total number of new firms attracted to Humberside because of the bridge has been limited and few new jobs have been created to offset the decline in traditional industries such as fishing and steel.

The response from manufacturing industry has been even less encouraging. Yet this situation is hardly surprising. The inevitable 'time-lag' while firms adjust to the bridge and the continuation of adverse economic conditions would appear to preclude such developments in the short-term. Many industries are not prepared to consider moves at the present time, while the attractions of Special Development Area status elsewhere may outweigh the benefits of Humberside's Development Area grants. The existence of the Humber Bridge has certainly strengthened Humberside's case to the potential developer; the lack of a bridge proved a negative factor in the past.

Between 1945 and 1981 neither North Humberside (population 450,000) nor South Humberside (365,000) had proved attractive to the expanding consumer product manufacture and service activities because neither sub-region by itself offered a sufficient local market. Now both the real and perceived distances between places on North and South Humberside have diminished and the two separate sub-regions have been united to form a single market area with a population of 800,000. This higher threshold population may prove far more attractive to some firms and may change perceptions of opportunities on Humberside.

The Humber Bridge also stands as the symbol of modern Humberside, presenting an image far removed from the traditional view of isolated small fishing communities so often portrayed by the media. Now Humberside can capitalise on the publicity value of the world's longest single-span suspension bridge to convey a more accurate impression of a region with land for development, good links with Europe, vastly improved road communications and a still pleasant environment. To achieve this, however, the Humber Bridge will need to engender a new spirit of mutual co-operation among local authorities on the north and south banks which will overcome traditional suspicions and rivalries.

A further and as yet under-exploited aspect of the Humber Bridge is its potential as a stimulus to tourism, an activity previously under-represented in the regional economy despite the existence of coastal resorts such as Bridlington and Cleethorpes (North, 1981). Throughout history people have flocked to see the 'biggest and best' and the Humber Bridge proved no exception; however, the tourist potential of the bridge and its environs has not been fully exploited.

There is also considerable scope for exploiting the recreational potential of the bridge environs. These could become the focus of a regional scale leisure complex extending along both banks of the estuary. Former clay pits at Barton, now water-filled, are already used for various sports including angling, sailing and water-skiing and there is now a Country Park by the Humber Bridge. Other land-based activities could be accommodated at the more spacious and undulating north bank site. Early in 1984 proposals for a 'Theme Park' type development were mooted.

To date, legal obligations and the complexities of local government organisation have meant that no single authority had a brief to promote the tourist potential of the Humber Bridge. Humberside County Council has now drawn up plans based on some of the above ideas, and these will figure prominently in future submissions for EEC regional assistance, especially if the County is granted special Integrated Operations Area status.

Humberside Airport, situated some fifteen kilometres south of the bridge, became an immediate beneficiary of the bridge's opening. Until 1981 its catchment area had been largely restricted to South Humberside; now most of the north bank of the Humber is less than forty-five minutes driving time from the airport (Andrew, 1983). Passenger traffic has shown a marked increase since 1981 and exceeded 125,000 per year for the first time in 1985.

Finally, it should be noted that the Humber Bridge has significantly increased opportunities for shopping, cultural and entertainment, and recreational trips by Humberside residents. It is difficult to make any meaningful assessment of the impact of the Humber Bridge even six years after its opening. The harsh economic analysis from traffic and revenue statistics have simply fuelled the controversy surrounding the bridge, whilst the indirect benefits accruing from it have been difficult to quantify. By the end of 1987 over 21.3 million vehicle crossings had been made, yielding toll revenues of more than £34 million. Yet the financial plight of the bridge has escalated, with the overall debt reaching £300 million in December 1987. Accordingly, the Bridge Board was forced to raise tolls to the maximum levels permitted under the existing toll order. Private cars are now charged £1.50 per single crossing. Approval for higher toll charges must now be sought from the Government. If the proposed new toll charges are acceptable, the Government may consider writing off sufficient of the bridge debt to enable total repayment to be achieved by 2042. However, such an agreement is by no means certain. Without prompt intervention on this issue, the bridge debt is likely to grow by a further £30 million in 1988 alone.

A Government decision to write off even part of the mounting capital debt would give a welcome boost to the much-maligned Humber Bridge. Unless tolls can be reduced, the long campaign for a Humber crossing will have resulted in the replacement of a physical barrier by an economic one. Like any infrastructural investment, the Humber Bridge provides opportunities but it cannot create traffic, especially if toll charges act as a deterrent to usage. Yet it is possible to see the Humber Bridge as a positive investment for the future of Humberside. The bridge cannot by itself create growth within the region, especially in the short-term, but it can help to create a more suitable climate which will attract future development once national and local economic difficulties are overcome. The immediate impact of the bridge has undoubtedly been limited and highly localised, and its harsh economic baptism and infancy have seemingly vindicated the critics' arguments. However, Government intervention to reduce the overall capital debt could yield substantial benefits to a much wider area in the longer term. No great bridge has ever failed to justify its construction, and there is no reason to suppose that the Humber crossing will prove the exception.

Sources of Information — including References

Andrew, H.R. 'Humberside-Hull; a local authority airport', *Local Government Policy Making*, November 1983, pp. 71-3.

Appleton, J.H. 'Let's get the Humber Bridge plan into perspective', *Voice of Yorkshire & Humberside Industry*, August 1966, pp. 17-19.

Bowman, S. 'Roads come first for South Humberside', *Voice of Yorkshire & Humberside Industry*, April 1966, p. 25.

Brooke, D. 'The struggle between Hull and the North Eastern Railway, 1854-80', *Journal of Transport History*, September 1972.

Central Unit for Environmental Planning. *Humberside: A Feasibility Study*, H.M.S.O., 1969.

Crossman, R.H.S. *The Diaries of a Cabinet Minister*, Volume III, (Ed. J. Morgan) 1977.

Evans, E.W. 'The decision was purely a political one aimed at helping Labour win local votes', quoted by Turner, G. in 'The Humber crossing; a bridge too far', *Transport*, May/June 1981, p. 12-15.

Fox, Sir Douglas & Partners. *Transport Communication across the Humber estuary*, 1930.

Freight Transport Association. *Tolls policy — A memorandum to the Minister of Transport*, 1982. 6 pp.

House of Commons Committee Records. Select Committee on Railway Bills, Group III, 1873, *House of Commons Committee Records*, Volume 21, 1873.

House of Lords Committee Records. The Hull, South & West Junction Railway Bill, *House of Lords Committee Records*, Volume 23, 1873.

House of Lords Committee Records. The Hull & Lincoln Railway Bill, *House of Lords Committee Records*, Volumes 33/34, 1883.

Halcrow Fox & Associates. *Humber Bridge Toll Study*, 1977.

Hull Daily Mail. 'Mountains of debt on the bridge', September 20th, 1984.

Humber Bridge Board. *Monthly Traffic Reports*, June 1981 — June 1984.

Humberside County Council. 'Traffic crossing the Humber Bridge; origin and destination', *Report to Planning &*

Transportation Committee, September 14th, 1982.

Humberside County Council. *Humberside Facts & Figures,* 1984.

Humberside County Council. *Humberside Facts & Figures*, 1986.

Ingram, M.E. 'Communications', Chapter 13 in *History of Yorkshire, East Riding*, Victoria County History, 1969, p. 392.

James, J.H., Scott, S.F. & Wilatts, E.C. 'Land use and the changing power industry in England & Wales', *Geographical Journal*, 127, 1961 pp. 286-309.

Lewis, P. & Jones, P.N. *The Humberside Region*, 1970.

North, J. 'The Humber crossing; an unfinished saga', Chapter 6, pp. 51-61 in Symes, D.G. ed. *North Humberside Themes*, Hull, 1978.

North, J. 'The Humber Bridge; bridge of opportunity', *Transport*, September/October 1981, pp. 27-8.

North, J. 'Bridging the gaps and clearing the air', *Transport,* March/April 1982, p. 43.

North, J. 'Humber Bridge pre-paid ticket sales', unpublished paper, 1984 (a).

North, J. 'Responses to the Humber Bridge: A survey of 200 commercial firms', unpublished paper, 1984 (b).

Thomas, R.E. 'The Humber Bridge: Prospects and Implications', paper given at *Cashing in on the Humber Bridge* Conference, Scunthorpe, 1982.

Tuckwell, R.M. *Return on the Bridge: A review of the economic prospects of the Humber Bridge*, 1983.

Turner, G. 'The Humber crossing — a bridge too far?', *Transport*, May/June 1981, pp. 12-15.

Ward, F.W. 'Bridging both banks', *Voice of Yorkshire & Humberside Industry*, October 1967, p. 32.

VII

The Humber Estuary and industrial development

(A)   Historical

Joyce Bellamy

Introduction

1.   The early nineteenth century

2.   The mid-nineteenth century

3.   Mid-century to the first world war

4.   The inter-war years

Introduction

On the eve of the nineteenth century the increasing industrialisation of Britain stimulated the demand for raw materials. Many
of these originated in Northern Europe so the Humber Estuary,
and particularly the port of Hull with a long tradition of
mercantile connections in Baltic ports, became a natural location
for this traffic.[1]* Some of the commodities were also handled at
Grimsby and Barton on the south bank, but apart from Hessle,
where ships were built and whiting also made,[2] the other estuarial
communities were largely undeveloped in maritime activities.
Goole at this period comprised 'isolated farms set in a regularly
enclosed field pattern largely conditioned by a network of inter-

---

*   Figures refer to notes at the end of this contribution.

locking field drains'[3] and the medieval port of Immingham had become silted, as had the haven leading to the ancient borough of Hedon.

The industrial use of the estuary from 1800 to the Second World War is considered here in four sections. The first describes the early years of the nineteenth century; the second examines the position at mid-century and the third reviews the main developments to the eve of the First World War. The fourth considers the inter-war years.

1.   The early nineteenth century

Hull was the estuarial focal point for river and coasting traffic and overseas trade. Its first dock — subsequently known as Queen's Dock — had been opened by the Hull Dock Company in 1778 and in 1800 there were 611 vessels, totalling 68,533 tons registered at the port. Some 300 master mariners were resident locally and at least another 300 persons associated with mercantile pursuits, either as general merchants or specialists in a particular commodity. The port's wood trade — a major sector of its commercial life — was organised by some twenty-five merchants. Hull was then among the main shipbuilding centres of the country.[4] Seven shipyards were located along the banks of the River Hull but some boat-builders operated from the Humber bank. Craft were being supplied for the merchant fleets and, as Hull was then Britain's principal whaling port, some of the ships which sailed to the Northern Whale Fishery had come from local yards.

Among the imported goods were flax, hemp, linseed, tallow, tow and tar, all mainly from Russia, rapeseed from Denmark, bar iron from Sweden and turpentine from America. Barilla (a carbonate of soda used in hard soap and glass manufacture), cork and dried fruits came from the Mediterranean. Bristles were imported from Prussia and Russia, dyestuffs (especially smalts, used in linen, paper and starch manufacture and for staining earthenware, glass and porcelain) came mainly from Germany and Norway and clover-seed, hides and wheat, primarily from Germany and Prussia but also from Holland.

Already the nucleus of much of Hull's later industrial

development was apparent. Several oilmills were crushing the linseed and rapeseed to produce oil which could then be used with turpentine to make colours; hemp was needed for roperies in Hull and Barton and the iron foundry of John Todd and Duncan Campbell in Cannon Street, Hull (later known as the Old Foundry) was supplying customers with German millstones and Dutch tarras (a rock for making mortar or hydraulic cement).

Experiments with steam engines were being made by a Richard Witty but the application of the steam engine to corn, oil and saw mills was, as elsewhere, slow. However, the potentialities of the port for industrial activities, based especially on the availability of raw materials, induced several businessmen to settle in Hull at this time. John Holmes came from Doncaster in 1800 to start his tannery by the River Hull and subsequent members of his family were involved in leather-belting and marine engineering. Thomas Sissons, a native of Market Weighton, took over an old colour firm and, with his brother Richard, made Sissons and Co. into one of the two principal Hull paint manufacturers. The other firm was Blundell, Spence and Co. founded by Henry Blundell, born in Lincoln, who was apprenticed to a brushmaker in Hull and in 1810 commenced on his own; after three years he was also in the colour trade and became one of Hull's most prominent businessmen and local activists. George and Thomas Earle, from York, started as Russia merchants in 1809 — the year when Hull's second dock was opened. By the 1820s they were making cement from imported raw materials, a business which was considerably extended later in the century.

At Grimsby, where the haven from the Freshney River had earlier been destroyed by silting, a new dock was opened in 1800 by the Grimsby Haven Company but the absence of a pier near its entrance deterred some shipmasters,[5] especially in the winter, although imports of timber, tar, linseed, wheat and other commodities were handled. In 1802 the town's convenient location to the Dogger Bank fishing grounds was advertised,[6] but a lack of communications with its hinterland prevented the development of the fishing industry at that time.

At Barton, which had ferry services to the north bank,[7] members of the Hall family had engaged in rope-making as early as 1767.[8] It was John Hall (1775-1863) who made the greatest contribution to the growth of the business and in 1808 obtained a patent for making ropes and cordage for the Navy.

Hull's predominance in the estuarial economy at the beginning of the century is revealed by the comparison of its population with the other communities shown in Table 7.1, and not surprisingly, it was to the long-established port that potential businessmen were attracted. But by the mid-century Hull was beginning to experience competition in some of its traditional import and export trades, although it remained the principal location for much of the estuarial industrial development until the mid-twentieth century.

Table 7.1

Population Trends 1801-1951

	1801	%	1851	%	1911	%	1931	%	1951	%
Hull	29580	86	87931	83	277991	67	313649	68	299105	64
Grimsby	1524	4	8860	8	77052	19	92458	19	94557	20
Cleethorpes	284	1	839	1	21450	5	28621	6	29557	6
Barton	1709	5	3866	4	6673	2	6332	1	6232	1
Immingham	144	...	242	...	2681	1	2423	1	2803	1
Goole	294	1	2960	3	20332	5	20239	4	19234	4
Hessle	681	2	1576	1	5319	1	6559	1	12913	3
	34216	99*	106274	100	411498	100	470281	100	464401	99*

Sources: Population Census data and A.R. Tailby, *The Story of a Village: Immingham* (1970).

... = less than 1%

*does not add up to 100 on account of rounding.

2. The mid-nineteenth century

The estuary's first rail link with the rest of the country was opened in 1840 when the line from Hull to Selby was completed. Hull's dock facilities had been increased with the opening in 1829 of the Junction (later Prince's) Dock which linked the original dock with the Humber Dock. This was followed by the Railway Dock in 1846 and the Victoria Dock in 1850. But there was some evidence that the port's trade, as shown by its shipping tonnages, was affected not only by the 1847/8 depression in the British economy but possibly also by competition from other Humber ports. The Hull Dock Company admitted in its *Annual Report* for 1850 that whereas the trade of the ports of Goole, Grimsby and Gainsborough (on the Trent) had greatly increased, that of Hull 'has been nearly stationary for the last five years'. The factors which gave rise to this situation may have been complex but the creation of the port of Goole by the Aire and Calder Navigation in the mid-1820s was certainly one of them. It had been developed largely for the trans-shipment of export traffic from West Riding towns and in 1848 had its own rail link when the railway between Goole and Wakefield was completed. By mid-century its population had risen tenfold. About a quarter of its workers were involved with dock and river activities and the port had several shipyards, a foundry and a brewery.

At Grimsby it was not until the second half of the 1840s when new dock works were under way and the port's first railway services provided — with connections to Boston, Market Rasen and Lincoln in 1848 and to Sheffield in 1849 — that its population rose rapidly. It was realised that Grimsby's favourable location for exploiting the North Sea fishing grounds — which had begun from Hull by the mid-1840s[9] — could not succeed until direct rail communication with London was achieved. A new dock was opened in 1852 but to cater for the fish trade the Manchester, Sheffield and Lincolnshire Railway which served the port, had a dock built specifically for fishing smacks which was opened in 1857, and extended in 1866.

The merchants at Hull were always sensitive to developments elsewhere in the estuary. There had been consternation when the Aire and Calder Company decided to develop Goole as a port. Local pressure for a third dock ensued but conflict occurred between the Hull Dock Company, whose members wanted to tax the river traffic, and the local merchants who objected to paying the dues. In 1825 the *Hull Rockingham* pleaded with the leading interests in the town to 'lay aside all animosity and try what can be done' — a point of view which was to be re-echoed throughout the century in relation to the provision of dock and transport facilities. So when it had become very clear that by mid-century

Hull's trade was being affected there was much local agitation, lead by Henry Blundell, for the reduction of dock dues to counter competition — not only from the estuary ports — but also from others on the East Coast. The outcome was a Dock Dues Bill which became law in 1852 and resulted in substantial reductions in the dues charged by Trinity House and the Hull Dock Company and the abolition of water-bailiff dues charged by Hull Corporation.

Hull at this time was unable to develop a coal export trade because of the absence of a direct rail link between the port and the Yorkshire coalfield. An attempt had been made in 1845 when a Hull and Barnsley Railway Company was promoted but this failed and in the same year the Hull and Selby Railway was leased to the York and North Midland Railway, which became part of the North Eastern Railway Co. in 1854. This loss of control over the rail connections from Hull to the national network made the port dependent, until the opening of the Hull and Barnsley Railway in 1885, on the policies of a company with other port connections — which included Hartlepool — and was the cause of constant complaint during subsequent decades.

Up to the late 1830s Hull's industrial base had hardly changed but its shipbuilding and whaling activities had declined. The former was affected by competition from yards in the North, especially Sunderland, and the industry appeared to be leaving the port by mid-century. The latter had reached its peak in 1818/19 when over sixty ships sailed to the whaling grounds but in 1851 only twelve went out. When the *Diana* was lost in 1869 the trade ceased. During the early decades whaling was important in the local economy. The blubber was boiled at the Greenland yards on the banks of the River Hull and the oil produced was used for lamps but also in various branches of manufacture.

A pottery — known as the Belle Vue Pottery — was begun on the Humber bank at Hull with its own wharf for unloading china clay and coal and for exporting its products, mainly to the Continent.[10] But when the Hull to Selby Railway was constructed it lost its essential estuarial access and by 1841 had closed.

In the 1820s the volume of cotton goods being shipped from Hull increased substantially. This trend continued into the next decade and induced some local merchants to introduce cotton manufacture to the port. The Hull Flax and Cotton Mill was opened in 1838 and the Kingston Cotton Mill ten years later.[11] The 1851 Census showed that Hull had 2235 men, women and children employed in the industry, a large number of whom came from the cotton districts of Lancashire and Cheshire but also from Ireland and elsewhere in Britain. The original workers arrived 'by boatloads' as the first mill opened before the Hull to Selby line was in operation. Most of them lived near the mills which were adjacent to the River Hull. A number of local people also obtained work in this new industry.

The beginning of the trawl-fishing industry was, however, to be of greater significance in the subsequent economy of Hull. During the 1830s trawling smacks from Devon and Kent were fishing in the North Sea and Hull and Scarborough were used as 'summer trawling stations' but it seems most likely that the opening of the railway to Hull in 1840 was the main factor in stimulating the growth of the industry there. Between twenty and forty smacks were sailing from the port in the 1840s and by mid-century Hull had 42 fishmongers and six fish wholesalers — pioneers of the later trade — one of whom, William Carr was importing block ice from Norway.

Of particular significance for subsequent industrial growth were the developments occurring in the shipbuilding and shipping sectors. The Junction Foundry in Waterhouse Lane, Hull, previously occupied by James Livingston, a whitesmith who had built an iron steamboat there in 1831 and which was launched from a yard on the Humber bank, was taken over in 1845 by Charles and William Earle, sons of Thomas Earle, the cement manufacturer. By 1851 the Earle brothers had laid out a shipyard at the east end of Victoria Dock and were employing seventy-two men. Two years later they launched their first ship, an iron screw steamship, of 100 tons. Martin Samuelson, employing 70 men in 1851, took over one of the old shipyards along the River Hull and in 1854 launched his first ship of 650 tons. He had been joined by his brother, Alexander and a Hull solicitor, W.H. Moss, whose wife was a daughter of Henry Blundell. These new developments — and especially those of the Earle brothers — became linked with the enterprise of Hull-born Thomas Wilson, who had started in the 1820s as an iron merchant but in the late 1840s began to specialise in shipping and shipowning. Thomas was joined by his sons Charles and Arthur and the firm then extended their fleet, obtaining a number of their ships from the yard of C. & W. Earle. Important also for the subsequent economy of Hull was the arrival in 1840 of Isaac Reckitt, a native of Wainfleet, Lincolnshire who took over an old starch works; ten years later he was exhibiting his product at the Great Exhibition of 1851 and had a staff of 51 (23 men, 27 women and one boy). In 1843 James Forster, a local man, joined with Joseph Andrews of London to establish an organ-building works in the town. Both had been indentured to a London organ builder but with a scarcity of organ builders in the north of England and the facility of good timber supplies in Hull, their progress was rapid. By 1851 they had a branch in York and displayed an organ and a variety of organ pipes at the Great Exhibition of that year. The business closed in 1956 having built 1378 organs during its existence.

By mid-century, therefore, some diversification of Hull's maritime economy had occurred and, although varied, was somewhat small scale, especially in terms of employment — except for the cotton mills. Excluding these, Henry Blundell was probably the largest industrial employer with 350 workers. The Old Foundry had 50, Holmes's tannery, 40, W. & H. Hodge (from Kilnsea) seed crushers, 23 and the cement firm of G. & T. Earle had 19 workers. It was still Hull's mercantile activities which provided the largest employment opportunities, with some 6000 men engaged in work on the seas, rivers, docks and harbours, representing 23 per cent of total occupied males (Table 7.2a). Only 24 per cent of the female population was classified as officially occupied — compared with 65 per cent of the male and nearly half of these were in domestic or other service, about a fifth in dress trades and 13 per cent in textiles (mainly cotton) (Table 7.2b).

In proportional terms Barton and Hessle, compared to Goole and Grimsby, had not increased at the same rate (Table 7.1). Barton was not yet serviced by railway links although steam packets plied between the town's foreshore and Hessle, which was on the Hull and Selby railway line. Cleethorpes had begun to cater for the holiday needs of workers who came, initially by steam packet along the Humber,[12] and later by train but it also served as a dormitory for Grimsby's rapidly growing population.

By mid-century, therefore, while Hull was still the main centre of industrial activity, the creation of Goole and the new developments at Grimsby were attracting migrants to the Humber

Table 7.2a

Hull Occupation Structure: Male

	Percentages				
	1851	**1861**	**1881**	**1901**	**1911**
Transport	23	23	22	29	31
Metals, shipbuilding, engineering	8	12	12	12	13
Food	8	8	7	8	8
Building	8	8	9	10	7
Commerce	3	5	6	7	7
Oils, paints	2	3	4	4	5
Woodworking, timber	5	5	4	5	4
Labourers — unspecified	8	7	10	6	4
Fishing	1	1	3*	2	2
Textiles	7	5	2	1	1
(cotton)	(4)	(2)	...	—	—
	73	77	79	84	82

* not comparable with other years. In 1881 fishermen arriving in port during the following fourteen days were included.

Table 7.2b

Hull Occupation Structure: Female

	Percentages				
	1851	**1861**	**1881**	**1901**	**1911**
Domestic/other service	49	52	54	45	39
Dress	24	24	21	18	15
Food	3	3	4	7	10
Oils, paints	...	...	1	5	7
Professions	5	5	7	9	8
Commerce	—	—	...	1	3
Textiles	13	11	6	6	4
(cotton)	(12)	(10)	(3)	(2)	—
	94	95	93	91	86

... = less than 1%

Source: Census Occupation Tables

Estuary in considerable numbers.

3.   Mid-century to the first world war

During this period new docks were built; Albert, 1869, William Wright, 1880 and St Andrew's for the fish trade in 1883, all by the Hull Dock Company and, in 1885, the Alexandra Dock by the Hull and Barnsley Railway Company. In 1893 the London and North Eastern Railway took over the Hull Dock Company. Discussions for another dock — spurred on by plans for dock development at Immingham — produced the joint dock proposal between the LNER and the Hull and Barnsley which became the King George Dock in 1914. The Salt End Jetty near Paull was completed in the same year. Hull's registered tonnage in 1900 totalled 882 vessels of 241,635 tons; the port was ninth in national tonnage and the value of its overseas trade made it Britain's third port. This expansion was substantially assisted by the growth of the Wilson Line fleet. In 1903 when T. Wilson, Sons and Co. Ltd took over the Bailey and Leetham ships, the Wilsons had 105 steamers, totalling 170,000 tons, 70 per cent of the port's tonnage. The Wilson line was taken over by Sir John Ellerman in 1916.

The attempt to diversify Hull's industrial structure by cotton manufacture failed. The first mill was liquidated in 1857, reconstructed in 1860 but closed down in the mid-1870s. The second mill ceased production in the early 1860s through lack of supplies during the American Civil War but on re-opening was not profitable and was compulsorily liquidated in 1894. The role of the location factor in their failure is indeterminate: cotton manufacture might have prospered on Humberside if it had been established on a firmer financial structure and managed by more experienced men.

The inter-dependence between the principal industrial sectors increased in the second half of the century, especially in the shipping, shipbuilding, marine engineering and fishing industries and also in oilseed crushing and paint manufacture. Further examples of family influences were apparent, particularly in tanning and leather belting, and the earlier tendency of workers to become their own masters continued; in this respect Martin Samuelson and C. & W. Earle provided training grounds. The former created a graving dock at the mouth of the River Hull on land reclaimed from the Humber in the late 1850s which became known as 'Sammy's Point'. Both sailing and steamships were built there but the business, converted to the Humber Ironworks and Shipbuilding Co. Ltd in 1864 for financial reasons, failed in the following year. In 1872 this was taken over by Bailey and Leetham to repair their own ships. At least eighty ships had been launched from the Samuelson yard, but the Earle brothers were more successful. They acquired 47 acres near Victoria Dock in 1863, established a yard there and could launch their ships directly into the Humber. On Charles Earle's death in 1870 the business was made into a public limited company. With the development of the triple expansion engine and steel in ships, production increased and, in 1880, 3000 men were being employed. In the 1870s orders for the Wilson Line accounted for 39 per cent of total output but some naval ships involved Earles in severe financial losses. In 1900 the business was liquidated. It was then purchased by Charles Wilson in 1901 and conducted as a private company. In 1914 the peak output in the company's history was reached when 31,200 gross tons of shipping was built. Three of the company's employees, Cook, Welton and Gemmell, started on their own in 1883 at a yard on the Humber bank, near to Earles, and specialised in ships for the growing fishing industry. The firm had built 350 vessels before it left Hull in 1900 for a yard at Beverley.

With the arrival from Brixham of Robert Hellyer, among others, in the 1850s the fishing industry began to expand. Until this time the trade had poor facilities, with fish having to be landed near the ferry-boat pier in Nelson Street. When some smack-owners left Hull for Grimsby in the 1850s attracted by its new fish dock, the Hull Dock Company provided shed accommodation on the south-west quay of the Humber Dock where a daily fish market was held. Much of the fish caught was sent directly to London by fast cutters from the fishing grounds but when the charges for the carriage of fish by rail were reduced, the landings at Hull rose.

By 1867 some 260 smacks were using the port and only five vessels (a quarter of the daily arrivals) could be berthed at a time — compared with fifty at Grimsby — so Hull smack-owners pressed for improved facilities. After protracted negotiations they were permitted to use the newly-opened Albert Dock but it was not until 1883 that the trade had its own dock. Fishing vessel owner-ship was more widely spread than that of merchant shipping but towards the end of the century some consolidation took place.Several companies were formed to purchase steamships for fish-carrying and in 1890 the Hull fish merchants, of whom there were nearly a hundred, established their own protection association. With the formation of the Hull Fishing Vessel Owners' Association Ltd in 1892, the trawler owners had become a powerful pressure group and in 1894 were agitating for more dock accommodation and threatening to leave Hull. Attempts were made to obtain facilities at Grimsby and Boston but the former port could take no more vessels. A second fish dock had been completed at Grimsby in 1878 and in the mid-1890s the Manchester, Sheffield and Lincolnshire Railway, which served the port, agreed to provide more dock room there. The North Eastern Railway then sanctioned an extension to St Andrew's Dock which was opened in 1897 almost doubling the area for the Hull fishing industry. The demand for dock space had been exacerbated by the winter arrivals of Norwegian herring cutters, whose catches were unloaded at Hull.[13] The new fish dock at Grimsby was completed in 1900.

By 1900 in Hull the capital invested in steam trawlers was estimated at £1.4m and in three ice houses at £125,000. There were thirty premises for smoking fish and, with the ancillary trades, it was estimated that some 10,000 persons were involved directly in the industry, as trawlermen, workers in the shipyards and engineering firms, the smoke houses, the fish market, and in rope and twine spinning and net-making. The industry had, therefore, become a dominant factor in the port's economy, a situation equally applicable to Grimsby where in 1911 some 575 fishing vessels were using its docks.

Technological innovations wrought structural changes in several of the port's industries. The oilseed firms were particularly affected as were those involved in flour milling. The first complete British roller milling plant without the traditional millstones was built by Henry Simon in the late 1870s. One of the local pioneers in the new technology was Joseph Rank, whose grandfather, John Rank, a Sproatley flour miller came to Hull in 1841 and whose son James, continued the family tradition. In 1875 — a year when Hull's wheat imports exceeded previous levels and when the

Wilson shipping line had opened a direct service between Hull and New York — Joseph started on his own at a mill in Holderness Road. Towards the end of the 1870s some of the country millers (Thompsons of Skidby and Kirbys of Nafferton) settled in Hull, attracted by the availability of imported wheat. Between 1878 and 1883 flour imports from America doubled and local millers were forced to modernise their machinery. Simon's new method was introduced to Hull in 1884 and Joseph Rank soon used it. His Alexandra mill was opened in 1885 and his Clarence Mill, adjacent to the River Hull, in 1891, which enabled wheat cargoes to be unloaded from barges alongside the mill. A silo system for wheat storage was also adopted and by 1898 the demand for his products necessitated the erection of another mill; at the end of the century J. Rank Ltd was supplying at least half the locally-milled flour. At that time three West Riding firms, Rishworth, Ingleby and Lofthouse (later Spillers Ltd) transferred to a new mill, also adjacent to the River Hull.

By 1861 George and Thomas Earle were exporting 'vast cargoes of fine plaster and Roman and Portland cements' to Russia as well as supplying the growing home market. In the early 1860s cement was being used increasingly for the building of harbours, docks, waterways and railway bridges as well as for artificial stone. Earle's original site was located on the Humber bank but the Albert Dock construction necessitated a move and they chose a site at Wilmington, adjacent to the River Hull. Earle's continued to dominate the local trade and in 1897 adopted its own trademark — the Pelican.

New industrial developments included those of Thomas J. Smith, a pharmaceutical chemist from Northumberland who took over 61 Whitefriargate in 1856 where he specialised in drug whole-saling and the refining of cod liver oil. In 1880 he moved to South Church Side and in 1883 was awarded a gold medal for his cod liver oil at the Fisheries Exhibition of that year. In 1896 he took into partnership his nephew, H.N. Smith who had been trained in the textile industry and who assumed control of the business on his uncle's death a few months later. H.N. Smith decided to develop the surgical dressings side of the business, which enabled the firm to expand during the First World War.

There were also further examples of family influences. Shortly after T.J. Smith had settled in Hull, Joseph Henry Fenner, of

Bermondsey and a grandson of John Holmes, the tanner, started in Bishop Lane as a currier in 1861 and in two years was supplying leather strapping for steam engines. His uncle, Thomas Holmes had patented an improvement in these straps in 1855 and they were much used in the local factories and saw mills. Fenner's two sons extended the business and in 1891 moved to Marfleet, near the Humber bank where a factory was erected. In 1870 William Dent Priestman, whose father had come to Hull in the mid-1840s and had him apprenticed with Martin Samuelson, commenced in partnership with Richard Sizer as general engineers; the firm, subsequently known as Priestman Brothers when William's brother Samuel joined him, made dredging and excavating machinery and also experimented with petroleum engines, some of which were used to propel canal barges. Patents were obtained for these engines but this invention in the 1880s, prior to the Diesel engine — was not a financial success. By the end of the century the firm had reverted to its earlier products.

At the Old Foundry Mrs Rose (Duncan Campbell's daughter) had appointed a new manager, James Downs, an engineer from Glasgow, whose inventive skills and business abilities were responsible for the subsequent growth of the business. He became a partner shortly before Mrs Rose's death at a time when oilmill equipment was being exported to overseas markets as well as equipping local oilmills. Of the brass-founding firms one, under the control of Mrs M.A. Shipham for several decades, emerged as the principal local establishment. But a new industry, metal containers, began in the 1890s. Initially to provide tins for the paint industry, one of the firms, F. Atkins and Co. was later taken over by the Metal Box Company. This industry provided a welcome addition to much needed opportunities for female employment. As did the manufacture of confectionery started by Frederick Needler in 1886 and the expansion of Reckitt and Sons.

Another new industry for Hull was provided by the American Radiator Company from Buffalo, U.S.A. which decided to commence production in England. Operations started in Hull in 1906, the location having been chosen on account of raw material availability and proximity to European markets. Initially known as the National Radiator Company, the name was changed to Ideal Boilers and Radiators in the 1930s.

On the eve of the First World War, the trades and industries of

Hull accounted for 68 per cent of the total male labour force in the six main estuarial towns; for women it was 71 per cent; Grimsby's shares were 19 and 18 per cent respectively; Goole and Cleethorpes were identical with 5 per cent for males and 4 per cent for females and at Barton and Hessle the figures were 2 per cent and 1 per cent for males and 1 per cent and 2 per cent for females.

The Grimsby fishing industry was stimulated by additional dock facilities, railway services to London, readily available coal supplies from south Yorkshire and Nottinghamshire in addition to its proximity to the North Sea where its fishing activities were largely concentrated. Apart from the fish trade, its general commerce with Scandinavian and Baltic countries was extensive. In addition to its coal exports, manufactured goods were shipped overseas and timber, wood pulp (there was a local paper mill) and dairy produce were imported. In 1911 over 30 per cent of the male population was employed in dock and shipping activities — a similar proportion to Hull — with 13 per cent in food trades (including about 700 fishermen) and 8 per cent in ship- and boat-building.

The successful development of Grimsby encouraged the Great Central Railway to build the dock at Immingham where, in 1870, borings had shown it to be the best estuarial location for a deep-water dock.[14] The proposal met with some hostility from Grimsby initially but agreement was later reached to enable a light railway to connect the Grimsby and Immingham Docks. Between 1901 and 1911 Immingham's population rose tenfold but it was to be some fifty years before any extensive industrial development occurred in its vicinity. In the meantime, however, it was favourably placed to handle coal exports and Swedish and other imported ore for Scunthorpe, only some twenty-three miles away, where iron and steel manufacture was developed in the second half of the century.

At Goole in 1911 half of the employed males worked in transport activities. Apart from shipbuilding, general engineering and chemical manufacture, the port was very largely dependent on the trans-shipment of goods from canal to coastal and short-sea vessels, and especially in the handling of coal. Largely responsible for this was the development by W.H. Bartholomew, engineer to the Aire and Calder Navigation, of a compartment boat train system which was invaluable for the movement of coal on the Calder and Hebble and Barnsley canals. Coal exports from Hull

Table 7.3

Humber Coal Exports

	1880	%	1890	%	1900	%	1913	%
				'000 tons				
Hull	601	47	1014	45	2199	53	4729	52
Grimsby	363	28	663	29	1074	26	2984	33
Goole	314	25	584	26	897	21	1326	15
	1277*	100	2260*	100	4171*	100	9039	100

* components do not add up to total on account of rounding
Source: Annual Statements of Trade

reached a peak of over 4 million tons in 1913 but its share of total Humber coal exports declined slightly with the expansion of this trade at Grimsby (including Immingham dock which had opened in 1912) (Table 7.3).

Outside the port areas, estuarial industrial activities included brick- and tile-making along the south bank, especially in the vicinity of Barton but also from Burton Stather on the Trent, to the Humber bank at Killingholme; use was made of the local clay and the products were shipped from wharves near the yards.[15] At Barton the single most important industry on the eve of the First World War was cycle manufacture which employed nearly 500 men in 1911.

An outstanding feature of the historical industrial use of the Humber Estuary was the segregation of development and, as James Bird emphasised 'no one site and situation could supply all the locational advantages for traffic on this estuary . . . each of the ports suffers from some relative locational defect that has allowed other ports to co-exist with it . . . If Hull had been situated near Goole it would have been better placed to serve the West Riding. The slight disadvantage allowed Goole to develop. The poor water approaches to Goole ensured that it could never become the port dominating the estuary. Grimsby's distance from the main ebb-channel gave Immingham its chance to arise.[16]

4. The inter-war years

The fishing industry continued to dominate the economy of Grimsby — its fish dock space on the eve of the Second World War had a surface area of 63 acres, considerably larger than at Hull where the St Andrew's Dock and its extension was about 20 acres — although at Hull the industry was still an important feature of its industrial structure. Some of the older firms were expanding into new products: T.J. Smith & Nephew added medical goods and toiletries to its surgical dressings; Reckitt and Sons entered the pharmaceutical field and Ideal Boilers and Radiators began to manufacture sanitary ware. There were new developments in the paint trade and Hull maintained its position as the premier UK port for oilseed imports up to the Second World War. But the closure of Earle's shipbuilding company in 1932 was a severe shock to the town and especially to the people of east Hull. During its existence nearly 700 ships had been built at the yard and the loss of this training ground for skilled craftsmen reverberated in the economy for many years afterwards. Some shipbuilding did continue in Hull but on a much smaller scale and the industry was carried on at Beverley, Hessle and Paull on the north bank and also at Goole.

There were, however, new developments along the north bank of the Estuary. The earliest of these was the establishment of aircraft manufacture at Brough.[17] During the First World War experiments with seaplane production were being made in Leeds by Robert Blackburn, and the decision was taken to test the machines on land at Brough adjacent to the Humber with easy access to the Hull and Leeds railway line. A hangar and slipway were built and in the 1920s the firm concentrated its production there. Work for the Navy was undertaken and flying training provided. In 1934 an engine company was taken over, and the firm's name changed to Blackburn Aeroplane and Motor Co. Ltd. Three years later the flying boat production was transferred to Dumbarton, some diversification was introduced to include agricultural implements in the immediate post-war years but the company continues to specialise on contracts for the Navy.

In the late 1920s the Hull Distillery Company was formed to manufacture industrial alcohol. This became part of the Distillers Company in 1929 but retained its own name until after the Second

World War. The distillery was erected near Salt End Jetty and a chemical works, managed by British Industrial Solvents (another subsidiary of the Distillers Company) was built alongside. These developments were the precursors of an extensive estuarial industrial complex, on the north bank near Hedon.

Also in the 1920s the Bristol metal refining firm of Capper, Pass & Co. was looking for a new location. A site at Melton on the north bank was chosen which was spacious, level, had access to rail facilities, water for cooling and discharge, old clay pits for dumping slag, coal supplies and ample labour. The firm commenced production in 1936/7 and this estuarial development has been further extended in the post-war years. Also located there was a cement works, formerly worked by the Humber Portland Cement Company but purchased by G. & T. Earle in 1923.

Apart from these developments, however, the inter-war years in the estuarial towns had few new employment opportunities. But the pattern of industrial use of the Humber Estuary was on the eve of substantial change and especially on the south bank where the facilities at Immingham — under-used in the inter-war years — were to become the centre of a large industrial complex after the Second World War.

Notes and references

1. J.M. Bellamy, *The Trade and Shipping of Nineteenth-Century Hull* (East Yorkshire Local History Society, no. 27: 1971, repr. 1979) p. 5.
2. G. Jackson, *Hull in the Eighteenth Century* (Hull, 1972; reissued Hull University Press, 1986) pp. 181, 194.
3. J.D. Porteous, *The Company Town of Goole: an essay in urban genesis* (Occasional Papers in Geography, no. 12: University of Hull, 1969) p. 6.
4. J.M. Bellamy, 'Some Aspects of the Economy of Hull in the Nineteenth Century with Special Reference to Business History' (Hull University Ph.D., 1966) Part II, Appendices VII A and D for accounts of shipbuilding in Hull at this time.
5. E. Gillett, *A History of Grimsby* (Hull 1970; repr. Hull University Press, 1986) p. 169.
6. Ibid., 177.

7. A. Harris, 'The Humber Ferries, and the Rise of New Holland, 1800-1860', *East Midland Geographer*, vol. 2 (1958-61) 11-19.

8. *The Story of the Hall-Mark* revised ed. (Stockport, 1975) p. 2.

9. There are conflicting accounts for the discovery of a rich source of soles (Bellamy thesis, Part II, Appendix IV) but I am indebted to Dr Robb Robinson for a press report in the *Leeds Mercury*, 20 Jan. 1845 which refers to the exploitation of the North Sea fishing grounds.

10. J. Bartlett and D. Brooks, *Hull Pottery* (Hull Museums Bulletin, Sept. 1970) p. 4.

11. Bellamy thesis, op.cit. Part II, Appendix II for details of the cotton industry.

12. R.W. Ambler, 'Cleethorpes: the development of an East Coast Resort', in *Ports and Resorts in the Region* (papers submitted to a conference in July 1980) ed. E.M. Sigsworth [1981] p. 180.

13. I am indebted to Dr Robb Robinson for this information from his thesis, 'The English Fishing Industry 1790-1914: a case study of the Yorkshire Coast' (Hull University Ph.D., 1985) p. 288 and to Dr R.W. Ambler for details of the fishing dock developments at Grimsby.

14. A.R. Tailby, *The Story of a Village: Immingham* (1970) p. 39.

15. N.R. Wright, *Lincolnshire Towns and Industry 1700-1914* (Lincoln, 1982) p. 204 ff.

16. J. Bird, *The Major Seaports of the United Kingdom* (1963) pp. 148-9.

17. Blackburn Aircraft Ltd, *The Blackburn Story 1909-1959* (Hull, 1960) pp. 12-13.

VII

The Humber estuary and industrial development

(B)   The post-war years

P.N. Jones

Introduction

1.   The geographical distribution of industry

2.   The development phase

3.   The decline of the estuarial dream

4.   The future role of the estuary

Introduction

The previous contribution to this volume examined the role of the estuary and its port facilities in the establishment and growth of industries in the nineteenth and early twentieth centuries. This had led to the emergence of distinctive industrial structures in Hull and Grimsby by 1920, while other important facilities, such as Immingham Dock, had only recently been initiated. In comparison the inter-war period, although not devoid of interesting developments as Joyce Bellamy has indicated, was an era of relative stagnation and disappointment.

It is against this background that we must view the profound changes which have affected the industrial geography of Humberside in the post-war period. In particular many of the most exciting developments have the estuary as their focus, and in this section I propose to describe and evaluate the significance of the estuary itself in the industrial evolution of Humberside as a whole.

Looked at from the standpoint of the 1980s it is helpful to consider the estuary's role in terms of two broad phases, approximately divided by the late 1960s/early 1970s. Having done so we shall then be in a stronger position to make an assessment of the likely future role of the estuary in the attraction of industry to Humberside. However, it will be useful to begin by outlining some basic but nevertheless useful points about the overall importance of industry in the economic structure of the region.

1. The geographical distribution of industry

In 1981 manufacturing industry employed some 90,000 people in Humberside, which is 30% of the total occupied population. This employment is far from being evenly-distributed within the county, and calculations based on individual factory locations for the late 1970s indicate that 60% of this employment is concentrated in less than 40 square kilometres out of a county total of 3510. In the disposition of this employment the estuary plays a pivotal role, since in its lower reaches it links two of the three major nodes of industrial concentration at Hull and Grimsby, while the third node at Scunthorpe has been steadily developing its estuarine-oriented facilities. (For a full discussion of present industrial activities see Symes, 1987.)

There are about 1600 factories of all sizes in Humberside, but the great majority are very small and clustered closely together on industrial estates or in the older parts of the major towns, where they can benefit from the concentration of a dense labour supply and the presence of a whole range of urban services. However, about 40 factories are very large and employ over 500 persons as a minimum, and it is with this type of large factory that the industrial development of the estuary in the post-war period has been largely associated.

2. The development phase

While there is no magical significance in taking the date of 1969 to mark the end of the first post-war phase, it does represent the culmination of a massive and protracted period of industrial expansion within the region, and indeed nationally, although actual industrial employment in Great Britain had peaked a little earlier in 1966. Within Humberside industrial employment reached an all-time peak of around 120,000 at the end of the 1960s, but a background of rising unemployment in Humberside signalled the end of the good years, and this was consolidated by the confirmation of Intermediate Area status for Humberside in 1969.

The essential theme of the industrial expansion of Humberside in this phase was the attraction and further expansion of industries processing bulky materials at an early stage in the manufacturing sequence. As such it demonstrated a fundamental continuity with the historical processes of industrial location and growth outlined by Bellamy (previous section). Moreover, as before, there was a continued reliance on the processing of bulky materials imported through the estuary and its ports. A major contrast, however, is supplied by the enormous scale and external financing of the new wave of incoming plants attracted to the Humber Estuary, which has important contemporary repercussions.

The estuary has, therefore, played a key role in the industrial rejuvenation of the region in the post-war period, and the focus of this activity lay in the lower reaches of the estuary, down-river from Hull. In 1945 this was a zone of major physical potential for industrial expansion, possessing a deepwater channel and enormous areas of flat land for industrial sites. With the notable exception of the Salt End jetties and chemical plant, which were established in the 1920s, and the huge expanse of Immingham Dock and its piers, the lower estuary was a 'vacant lot'. Conseqently, while many of the traditional industries linked to material-imports received an important boost in the generally expansionary economic environment of the post-war period, including fishing, fish-processing, timber-based industries, paints and chemicals etc., these were all tightly concentrated in the older ports such as Hull, Grimsby or Goole. The most spectacular investments pioneered the use of new types of estuarial space in the lower estuary, particularly on the South Humber Bank, where the

153

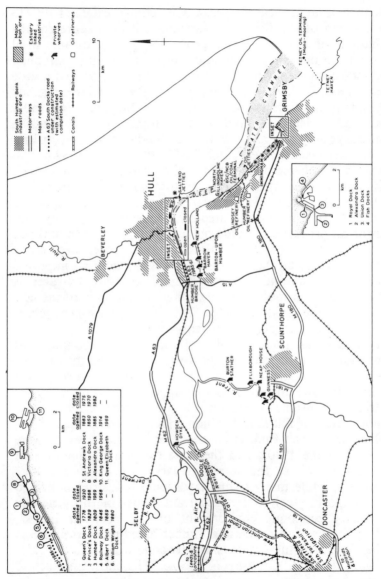

Figure 7.1 The Humber Estuary: communications and estuary-linked industrial sites.

deepwater channel in the estuary hugs the Bank. As Figure 7.1 shows, huge sprawling plants embodying the latest in industrial processes were established during the 1950s and 1960s, involved in industries as diverse as fertilizer manufacture, dyes and pigments, man-made fibres and oil-refining. As can be seen, the earliest arrivals tended to space themselves between Grimsby and Immingham, with each plant set in its own extensive 'estate', which acted as a reserve of land for future needs. Later, during the 1960s, the scale of construction increased still further and this led to developments to the north of Immingham.

In addition to the new plants set up on the South Humber Bank between 1950 and 1969 must be added the huge expansion of the Salt End works, and the establishment of many petroleum product storage depots. As the size of sea-going bulk and liquid carriers increased, especially in the 1960s, dredging in the Grimsby Roads together with the construction of massive terminals reaching out into the deepwater channel enabled the physical capacity of the estuary to adjust to all but the very largest vessels. Despite the many detailed differences in products and processes the new estuarial industries shared some common characteristics. Typically they are essentially 'upstream' activities, capital-intensive, and set up and controlled by firms from outside the region with few other connections in the region. They consumed enormous quantities of land (sites of 250 or 500 acres per plant are not uncommon) but provided proportionately few jobs, whether at the plants themselves or in the limited spin-off activities in the region. Acting as self-contained production plants for the most part, their function has been to transform as efficiently as possible bulky materials into manufactured products which are then sent elsewhere in Britain or overseas for further elaboration. As such they form an immediate contrast to the dense conglomeration of inter-linked industries and firms which developed around the traditional materials-processing industries of centres such as Hull.

The late 1960s represent in some respects the high-water mark of the role of the estuary in all facets of the region's industrial life, since both the new and the old industries linked to the use of the transportation facilities were flourishing. Table 7.4 illustrates those industries which were in 1968 highly characteristic of Humberside compared to Great Britain as a whole, and also indicates their degree of relationship — whether direct or indirect

Table 7.4

Characteristic Industries of Humberside in 1967
(1958 SIC Classification)

I Direct estuary links	LQ	II Indirect links — historical, sales, purchases etc.	LQ
Bacon curing, meat & fish products	8.0	Cans, metal boxes	5.7
Animal & poultry foods	4.7	Rope, twine & net	4.5
Vegetable & animal oils, fats soaps, detergents	4.7	Fruit and vegetable products	3.0
Leather tanning, dressing	4.5	Wooden containers	2.9
Chemicals and dyes	3.4	Paints, printers' ink	2.5
Shipbuilding	3.4	Contractors' plant	2.5
Timber	3.2	Pharmaceuticals & toiletries	2.0
Grain-milling	2.9	Aircraft	1.8
Man-made fibres	2.6		
Marine engineering	1.6		
Oil refining (under construction)			

LQ = Location Quotient. See P.W. Lewis and P.N. Jones *Industrial Britain — the Humberside Region* (1970) p. 77.

with the estuarial facilities. Moreover, at this time plans were well advanced for the establishment of the Immingham Bulk Minerals terminal on the South Humber Bank, a facility which was designed to switch the sourcing of iron ores consumed at the giant Scunthorpe steel complex from the local ironstone to foreign imports. It appeared then that the long-term development of the region was becoming even more closely-integrated with the estuary. This trend reached its apogee in the grand plans laid out in the Humberside Feasibility Study of 1969, which was one of a number of such studies set up to investigate the development potential of the 'Maritime Industrial Area' concept, and which had as its model the frenetic growth of Rotterdam-Europort. A scenario of further industrial development linked to the lower estuary, and involving industries such as oil-refining, petro-

156

chemicals and associated industries such as plastics, did not seem inappropriate in the economic and technological context of the time. Depending on the scale of anticipated growth, the possibilities of land reclamation for industrial uses in locations such as Spurn Bight and Pyewipe were also raised.

3. The decline of the estuarial dream

Since this period the role of the estuary has been subjected to a number of important changes; not all have acted in the same direction but are sufficiently important in their impact to suggest that a re-evaluation is necessary. It is equally important to stress that there has been no major change in the physical characteristics of the estuary which might have influenced its industrial potential, such as a dramatic change in the nature of the navigation channel. Rather the changes stem from the economic and political contexts, and indeed some had their roots even in the years before 1970.

The 'Europort Model' envisaged as a platform for further regional industrial growth in the late 1960s contained within itself certain contradictions. Perhaps the foremost, in a region always chronically short of jobs, was the low job creation associated with the post-war capital intensive types of industries attracted to the estuary, which could be as low as 10-20 per acre — a mere one-tenth of the level linked to light industries. Moreover, the eagerly-anticipated 'downstream' offshoots of the earlier primary-processing industries such as oil-refining, including petrochemicals and plastics, were slow to materialise. This was due, for the most part, to over-optimistic and over-simplistic assumptions concerning the pattern of linkages between these types of activities, rather than to any inherent drawbacks with the Humberside situation. There were also indications from the experience of industries such as iron and steel that the next wave of technological investment in heavier processing industries would create job losses — the Anchor Project at Scunthorpe had already pointed the way.

During the 1970s the industries of Humberside, in common with those of the nation as a whole, came under intense competitive pressures. The harsher global context of trade has been further intensified by Britain's entry into the EEC. As a result of political developments the price of oil-derived energy and products rose many-fold. In this harsher arena all industrial companies have been forced to look closely at all aspects of their operations, a process which for the larger firms involves national and international assessments of plants and their competitiveness. Because of its older industrial structure it is a truism that the industrial shake-out in Britain has possessed a greater severity than most of our competitors, resulting in a massive 20% decline in manufacturing employment between 1970 and 1980. It was a decline which affected not only traditional labour-intensive industries such as textiles or motor vehicles, but also modern industries such as oil-refining or man-made fibres. Set against this background of deepening industrial crisis there has been a tendency for the estuary itself to be intimately concerned with those industries in Humberside which have lost their growth momentum as a result of externally-induced circumstances rather than any major deficiencies in the potential of the estuary. Thus the huge decline of the fishing industry, and its accompanying adverse impacts on processing and ancillary industries in Hull and Grimsby, has been due primarily to the politically-dictated loss of distant-water fishing grounds. The contraction of the Scunthorpe iron and steel industry has had immediate repercussions on the level of ore traffic handled in the estuary, though this loss has been recompensed by the growth of substantial coal exports at the Immingham Terminal. The apparently relentless climb in the demand for oil-based products was set into reverse by the 'Oil Shocks' of the 1970s, resulting in severe over-capacity in oil-refining and petrochemical plants based on oil-derived feedstocks throughout Western Europe. In the cutbacks in this sector Humberside has perhaps fared better than other UK regions. There have been few complete closures, although the rebuilt Nypro plant on Trent-side is a notable exception. Rather, there have been some partial closures of older processes within particular plants, and in some cases considerable expansion in investment and output, as in the oil-refineries. Nevertheless, employment has dropped considerably below the estimated 9000 jobs which existed in the South Humber Bank industrial zone in the mid-1970s, and few now believe wholeheartedly in the long-term development prospects of the typical lower estuarial type of processing plant as a foundation for future expansion. Indeed it seems as though the 'shining visions' of the 1960s may become the 'stranded whales' of the 1980s when the full impact of Middle Eastern industrialisation is felt in European markets. The development of tougher environmental legislation by the EEC could also pose severe problems of cost-effectiveness.

Fortunately the 1970s also witnessed some countervailing tendencies in the region which tended to broaden the range of locational attractions for industry. The most important was the improvement in road communications led by the deep penetration of motorways on both banks, and capped by the Humber Bridge link. The latter increased the regional thresholds for service industries, labour supply and all other forms of economic activity. The rise in unemployment at the end of the 1960s also brought the region modest industrial assistance in the form of Intermediate Area status, and the rapid deterioration in the 1970s brought full Development Area status to the Hull and Grimsby travel to work areas (TWA); this status was soon extended to Scunthorpe in the aftermath of the steel cutbacks. Besides adding a useful source of financial aid for new and existing industrial expansion, government assisted area status in the 1970s enabled the provision of new 'light' industrial estates to be accelerated. In this respect the Sutton Fields Industrial Estate in North Hull is as typical of the Humberside of 1980 as the two giant oil refineries were of 1970. By the 1980s it may be suggested that, despite the restriction of full Development Area Status to Scunthorpe TWA, the range of locational attractions for industry in the region were unprecedentedly broad; the estuary and its ports and jetties have been supplemented by a substantial number of private riverside cargo wharves; many assisted industrial estates exist in the larger towns; the road network is improved beyond recognition. By the end of the 1970s Humberside was no more 'remote' from the nation's centres of population than Bristol or Manchester, and a small trickle of migrant firms had begun to arrive in the region. Yet unfortunately at this time the national economic crisis deepened into a full-scale depression, leaving any form of industrial expansion a rare and uncertain phenomenon. Over all hangs the shadow of exploding new microprocessor technology and computers — the so-called 'High Tech' or 'Sunrise' industries, upon which bandwagon all regions in Britain have been desperately trying to climb. What therefore of the region's industrial future, and of the estuary's part?

159

4. The future role of the estuary

The estuary, along with its accompanying marshlands, constitutes a magnificent physical asset and it is vital therefore to get the perspective right with respect to possible new developments. Even as late as the County Structure Plan of 1978 it seems as though industrial hopes were pinned firmly to the 'estuarial' banner. The Plan's insistence on reserving sites within the precious South Humber Bank Special Industrial Area for industries which have a compelling need to use the deepwater facilities (subsequently confirmed and indeed refined in the Revised Structure Plans of 1983 and 1985) is entirely defensible but further industrial expansion of the 1960s kind would imply more massive investments in capital-intensive plants and arguably a considerable degree of environmental damage, if only visual, for a diminishing return in jobs. Moreover, as the case histories of similar projects in areas such as Milford Haven indicates, these plants can have quite short life-spans.

The environmental hazards associated with large 'Special Industrial' plants have also become better documented and publicised during the 1970s. The experience of Flixborough, and the establishment of safety buffer zones and other safeguards, has also demonstrated the price which has to be paid for housing concentrations of these industries in the future.

I would therefore suggest that the future industrial prosperity of the region can be better served by a more circumspect and balanced appraisal of the estuary which recognises the real limitations of estuary-associated industrial schemes as well as the pay-offs. To this end three lines of development are important and ideally should proceed in tandem with carefully-regulated industrial schemes linked to the estuary.

    i.   The region's existing firms in whatever type of location should be encouraged to expand and strike deeper roots in the region. Most industrial studies conducted within the UK have stressed the vital importance of nurturing the already-established companies in all aspects of their activities.

   ii.   Existing efforts to attract new industries should obviously be continued, with a view to broadening the industrial base. This will include such industries as knitwear or clothing which provide valuable complementary job opportunities for females, as well as more diversified industries generally.

iii. Particular efforts should be made to connect the region with the new 'High Tech' industries and services, with their superior job creation prospects and potentially endless ramifications for all forms of economic activity. In view of the intense competition for these industries from all parts of Britain this will be no easy matter, although already examples exist of local firms becoming involved in the microelectronic revolution.

If the region is to have any realistic chance of making progress along these lines then a vital role must be allocated to upgrading the total environment of Humberside — in its physical, social, cultural and infrastructural contexts. It is a valid generalisation that throughout the present century manufacturing industry has been increasingly liberated from the older rigid locational constraints imposed by coal deposits, or mineral ores. This trend has not, however, been succeeded by a carefree freedom of choice. Instead we have witnessed the gradual insinuation of so-called 'behavioural' factors, which place stress on the many uncertainties and unquantifiable influences which enter into the entrepreneur's business decisions. Although the range of research findings is extensive, it points both to the importance of orthodox attractions, such as spacious and well-planned industrial 'parks', and to the significant subjective role played by an assessment of the quality of life offered by different locations for managers and other key personnel. To date the most pronounced beneficiaries of such trends seem to be the flourishing towns and smaller cities of south-east England. Within this context Humberside can offer abundant reserves of space, and a landscape which has been little-touched by the standardised blights of nineteenth-century industrialisation.

In cognisance of these underlying trends in locational attraction, the current Revision of the Humberside Structure Plan has placed great emphasis on the encouragement of a more dispersed pattern of industrial activity. This is reflected in recognising a need to provide a diversity of industrial estates in different types of locations and for a varied mixture of industrial firms. Inner cities, suburbs and country towns all feature prominently, as well as the major industrial sites of the estuary. It recognises also that a vision of the estuary's future as another kind of 'Super-Shellhaven' is outmoded and inaccurate. Can we take this a stage further, perhaps, and suggest that the Humber Estuary be looked upon as the centrepiece of a co-ordinated sequence of land-use planning and conservation schemes which could create a scene of great human animation and interest? As such the estuary would surely live up to its designation as the 'Heart' of Humberside.

References

Lewis, P.W. and Jones, P.N. *Industrial Britain — the Humberside Region* (1970). 235 pp. David & Charles.

Symes, D.G. Ed. *Humberside in the Eighties* (1987). 164 pp. Department of Geography, University of Hull.